Ideas from Mathematics Education

An Introduction for Mathematicians

Lara Alcock & Adrian Simpson

The Higher Education Academy: Maths, Stats & OR Network,
School of Mathematics,
The University of Birmingham,
Edgbaston,
Birmingham, B15 2TT.

www.mathstore.ac.uk

ISBN: 978-0-9555914-3-3

Acknowledgements

We would like to acknowledge the help and support of a number of people in preparing this book. In particular the Mathematics, Statistics and Operational Research (MSOR) Network who provided financial, website and publishing support. We would also like to thank the reviewers whose helpful and insightful comments considerably improved the text: Thomas Bartsch, James Blowey, Bill Cox, Eugenie Hunsicker, David Mond, David Tall and Brian Winn.

Lara Alcock and Adrian Simpson

Contents

Introduction

Our aim in writing these materials is to provide mathematicians with an accessible introduction to some ideas from mathematics education research. We could not do justice to the entire field in a document of this length, and we have not tried to do so. Rather, we focus on three ideas that we use to structure our thinking, as university mathematics lecturers, about what students need to learn in order to succeed in undergraduate mathematics. Specifically, we concentrate on what they need to learn in order to make sense of their early encounters with abstract definitions and proofs. In brief, the main points of the chapters are:

1. Definitions: *Students are often unaware of the status of formal definitions within mathematical theory and attempt to learn about concepts informally instead;*

2. Mathematical objects: *Many mathematical constructs can be understood as processes but need to be understood as objects in order for higher level reasoning to make sense;*

1

3. Two reasoning strategies: *We can distinguish two sensible ways of approaching a proof-related task; each demands a range of skills and some individuals may have preferences for one or the other.*

Each of these ideas provides us with a lens through which to view our students' thinking and, rather than having to consider 200 students with, potentially, 200 different ways of thinking, we can consider two or three broad categories of ways they might respond to the mathematics they encounter.

Our discussion of each of these issues is based on research involving close observations of students' learning of undergraduate mathematics. We include a number of quotations from students to illustrate their thinking; the majority of these are relatively successful students from high ranking institutions. We have found it illuminating to ask students to think aloud, without interruption, as they work on mathematical tasks. This often uncovers fragility in the knowledge of even the strongest students.

This document is very much about theories of learning *mathematics*, as opposed to general theories of learning or generic advice on "good practice" in teaching. We believe that this is important because the mathematical content is central to a lecturer's work in constructing lectures, notes, problem sheets etc., and because understanding students' likely interpretations of this content is therefore directly relevant to this day-to-day design work. We find these ideas helpful in planning our own teaching and in responding to students' individual questions, because they allow us to think systematically about underlying difficulties that manifest themselves in a variety of misunderstandings and errors. This systematic thought does not, of course, mean that there is a unique "best way to teach", but many teaching strategies can be thought of in terms of how they address the issues raised, and throughout the three chapters we provide specific illustrations of things that we and others have tried in our classes and research.

In presenting these ideas we hope to show that students face genuine challenges in learning to think like mathematicians and that some of the difficulties they face are inherent in making the transition to undergraduate mathematics, and are not attributable solely to lack of effort or preparation. We also hope to convey our belief that these difficulties are not insurmountable, and that having more insight into students' thinking is interesting for its own sake, and can make the work of teaching easier and more enjoyable.

Chapter 1

Definitions

1.1 Introduction

Here are two tasks for you to try:

1. *Define* "chair". That is, give a set of properties so that:

   a) everything which is a chair has those properties;

   b) everything which has those properties is a chair;

   c) everything you might deduce from that set of properties holds for all chairs.

2. Without giving the formal definition, *describe* the notion of a basis of a vector space.

Task 1 is hard, if not impossible. Dictionaries give definitions of concepts such as "chair", but these are concise descriptions designed to capture pre-existing concepts; they do not, and are not designed to, satisfy constraints (a), (b) and (c). Indeed, most of us have probably never looked at a dictionary definition of "chair", but our experience with chairs means that we have no problem recognising and using them in everyday life (Vinner, 1976; Vinner, 1991; Edwards & Ward, 2004).

Task 2, on the other hand, is relatively easy. It may be somewhat unsatisfying to give an informal description of a concept such as basis, because we know that in doing so we are glossing over technical subtleties. But most of us do such things regularly in our teaching and in talking to colleagues. When introducing the concept in a lecture, we probably provide a formal definition and also try to give students a sense of the concept by saying something like "as small a set of vectors as possible, from which you can make all the others in the space". Indeed, we move easily between informal statements that describe a concept and a formal definition that, unlike a dictionary definition, prescribes what is (and is not) an instance of that concept. We recognise, however, that there is a huge functional difference between the two types of statement, and that formal definitions serve to structure the world of mathematics precisely because they do satisfy constraints (a), (b) and (c).

Many new university students, however, are not aware of this difference. As a consequence, they often do not pay close attention to formal definitions and do not use these in their reasoning about abstract concepts, instead relying on *concept images* built up from their experience.

1.2 Concept Image and Concept Definition

Tall & Vinner (1981) used the terms *concept image* and *concept definition* to highlight the difference between the type of reasoning that is expected in advanced mathematics and the type that students often engage in. They used "concept definition" for what we might ordinarily think of as a mathematical definition, with an allowance that a student may not understand or remember this correctly, and "concept image" to describe much broader knowledge and experience with the concept:

> We shall regard the concept definition to be a form of words used to specify that concept. It may be learnt by an individual in a rote fashion or more meaningfully learnt and related to a greater or lesser degree to the concept as a whole. It may also be a personal reconstruction by the student of a definition.

> We shall use the term concept image to describe the total cognitive structure that is associated with the concept, which includes all the mental pictures and associated properties and processes. It is built up over the years through experiences of all kinds, changing as the individual meets new stimuli and matures. (Tall & Vinner, 1981, p.152)

The key point is that a mathematician would expect reasoning to involve the concept definition, either alone or in conjunction with the concept image, as illustrated in Figure 1.1 below. As Vinner puts it, "when a problem is posed to you in a technical

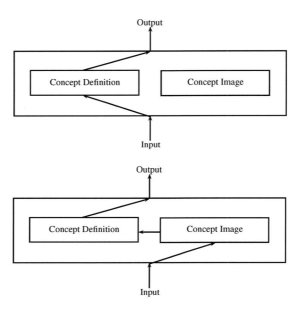

Figure 1.1: Reasoning using the concept definition

context, you are not supposed to formulate your solution before consulting the concept definition" (Vinner, 1991, p.72). However, students often respond as though they had consulted only their concept image, as in Figure 1.2. This does not automatically lead to incorrect answers, especially in relatively routine situations. But it does lead to incorrect answers in situations for which the student's concept image is less representative. We will give some examples of this phenomenon in the following sections.

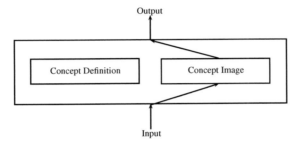

Figure 1.2: Reasoning using the concept image alone

1.2.1 Pre-existing concept images: functions and tangents

We can clearly see students using concept images rather than concept definitions when asking them to make judgements about whether something is or is not an instance of a concept. Errors (relative to the formal theory) are especially likely when students have a lot of experience with a concept but relatively little experience with its definition. For example, students encounter functions repeatedly in school mathematics with little, if any, concentration on a definition. When they come to university, they will often encounter a mathematical definition, with the (unwritten) expectation that this will now take precedence in making judgements and in drawing conclusions about functions. For many, however, it doesn't.

Vinner & Dreyfus (1989), for instance, asked students to judge whether or not certain graphs represented functions and whether functions existed with various properties, and to respond to the question "What is a function, in your opinion?" (Figure 1.3). Among those responding were 271 first year students on formal mathematics courses and 36 secondary school mathematics teachers, all of whom had been introduced to a formal definition.

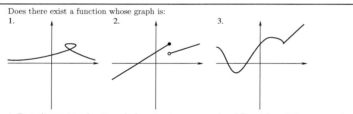

Does there exist a function whose graph is:

1. 2. 3.

4. Does there exist a function which assigns to every number different from 0 its square and to 0 it assigns 1?
5. Does there exist a function all of whose values are equal to each other?
6. Does there exist a function whose values for integral numbers are non-integral and whose values for non-integral numbers are integral?
7. What is a function, in your opinion?

Figure 1.3: Vinner & Dreyfus's questions about functions

Question	Students	Teachers
1	74	97
2	86	97
3	72	94
4	60	75
5	67	67
6	17	33

Figure 1.4: Percentages of students and teachers getting each question correct

Figure 1.4 shows that considerable proportions of both groups gave incorrect answers, especially to the question asking about a function which whose values are non-integral for integral numbers and vice versa. In response to the question asking respondents "What is a function, in your opinion?", significant numbers gave descriptions like "a dependence between two variables" or "an equation connecting two factors". Just over half did give a definition which had the characteristics of the standard Dirichlet-Bourbaki definition, but just under half of these did not appear to use the definition in making their judgements. Overall, this means that there was little use of the mathematical definition when making these judgments.

These results might be accounted for by considering features that are likely to form part of a student's concept image for function at this stage in their mathematical education. The majority of the functions they meet in earlier mathematics are at least continuous, if not smooth, and can be represented by a

single formula. If students rely on a concept image built up from
such earlier experience, rather than a more recently encountered
formal definition, it is not surprising that their judgements in
less "typical" cases are often incorrect.

Figure 1.5: Students were asked to indicate tangents at point P

A similar phenomenon can be found in many other areas.
Vinner (1991) also investigated students' understanding of the
concept of tangent in a similar way. Students, who had attended
courses giving definitions of a tangent in terms of limits of secants or as a line with a common point to the function graph
with slope equal to the derivative at that point, were asked to
consider Figure 1.5, and to choose between:

1. Through P it is possible to draw exactly one tangent to
   the curve (draw it).

2. Through P it is possible to draw more than one tangent
   (specify how many, one, two, three, infinitely many. Draw
   all of them in the case their number is finite and some of
   them in the case that it is infinite).

3. It is impossible to draw through P a tangent to the curve (Vinner, 1991, p.76).

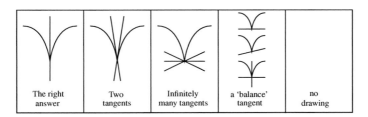

Figure 1.6: Tangent responses

Only 8% gave a reasonable drawing and the answer which would be considered correct from the limits of secants definition. The two-solutions or infinitely-many-solutions were each more frequent (as in Figure 1.6), with the remainder giving no response. With the definition in terms of derivative, the "no drawing" response may indicate students with a mathematically valid interpretation. However, the interesting issue is the 50% of students who gave the other responses. Again, this may be accounted for in terms of a concept image built upon students' earlier experience. In the case of the tangent concept, this is likely to have included lots of examples of tangents to circles, which don't "pass through" the graph, and/or tangents which are seen to somehow "balance" the graph locally.

1.2.2 Spontaneous conceptions based on everyday language: limits

We have seen that a pre-existing concept image can lead students to associate inappropriate features with a general concept, and can interfere with learning to use new formal definitions. A similar effect can occur when the words we use for our concepts are taken (for sensible reasons) from everyday language. Such use can lead to *spontaneous conceptions* (Cornu, 1991) or *naïve conceptualizations* (Davis & Vinner, 1986) that are at odds with the mathematical meanings. For example, initial encounters with the concept of limit are littered with words which bring with them a range of different associations, many of which may be quite inappropriate. A lecturer might take all of the following to mean the same thing (a convenient shorthand which, in each case, is expected to evoke the same precise formulation of the definition of convergence of sequences):

- The limit of (a_n) as n tends to infinity is a.

- (a_n) tends to a as n tends to infinity.

- (a_n) converges to a.

- (a_n) approaches a.

Robert (1982) noted, however, that the language used can evoke subtly different images. Some formulations, like *converge*, suggest a dynamism or movement, whereas others, like *the limit. . . is* seem static. Words like *approaches* suggest that the sequence cannot "go beyond" a limit, nor can it "reach" it.

Monaghan (1991) explicitly explored the ambiguity of this language by asking A-level mathematics students (amongst other things) what is true of the sequence $0.9, 0.99, 0.999, \ldots$

- it tends to $0.\dot{9}$

- it tends to 1

- it approaches $0.\dot{9}$

- it approaches 1

- it converges to $0.\dot{9}$

- it converges to 1

- its limit is $0.\dot{9}$

- its limit is 1

Leaving aside the issue of whether they recognise that $0.\dot{9} = 1$, the students gave quite different responses to the different forms of language. 74% said the sequence tended to 1, but only 36% affirmed that the limit was 1. Monaghan suggested the problem may stem from the imagery associated with the language: *limit* (as in a "speed limit") is something one should not exceed, or a boundary, while *tends to* suggests a trend towards something. A number of authors have provided illuminating quotes from students that give an indication of the range of interpretations of these terms:

"A limit is a boundary beyond which the sequence cannot go. But it has some important differences. A speed limit, like one on the highway, defines only a point beyond which you are not supposed to go. But the limit of a sequence is never reached by that sequence." (Davis & Vinner, 1986, p.296)

"$s_n \to s$ means s_n gets close to s as n gets large, but does not actually reach s until infinity." (Tall & Vinner, 1981, p.159)

"I don't really see how numbers can converge. Converge means light from a thing coming in. It's two separate parts. You'd have to have two sequences coming in on each other. I don't think you can have one sequence converging." (Monaghan, 1991, p.23)

1.2.3   Opposites and extensions: increasing and continuous

In the above illustrations, we have seen that students often use their concept images, rather than appropriate concept definitions, to make judgements about concepts. Some aspects of these concept images may come from previous experience with the mathematical concepts, and some from everyday use of mathematical terminology. In the latter case, the situation can be even worse than in the example given above, since in some cases language-based spontaneous conceptions can lead to strong intuitions against the consequences of the concept definition.

A good example of this effect is provided by "opposites". In everyday language use, something cannot be both increasing and decreasing. Something cannot be both open and closed. Some formal mathematical definitions, however, allow these everyday "impossibilities". This leads to all sorts of classification errors relative to formal theories. In our experience, faced with a request to give an example of a sequence that is both increasing and decreasing, as few as 20% of students are able to do so correctly, even with the definitions in front of them. The majority either state that this is impossible, or give an "alternating" sequence like $1, 0, 1, 0, \ldots$. This is hardly surprising if we suppose that instead of consulting the definitions, the students are simply using a sensible everyday interpretation of "increasing and decreasing". Indeed, while students do not have a problem classifying $1, 2, 3, \ldots$ as an increasing sequence, few are initially willing to accept $1, 1, 1, \ldots$ as such. This also is hardly surprising – it certainly seems unlikely that, without explicit encouragement, someone would include a constant sequence in their set of examples of increasing sequences. However, this is a serious point: students are often quite upset to realise that this is apparently what the formal definition dictates (Tall & Vinner, 1981).

Such conflicts between a concept image and concept definition can also occur when a definition which was historically formulated to capture familiar cases is then applied to a broader class of examples. For instance, the definition of continuity allows that the function

$$f(x) = \begin{cases} x & x \in \mathbb{Q} \\ 0 & x \notin \mathbb{Q} \end{cases}$$

is continuous at exactly one point. Even worse, any real-valued function defined solely on the integers is continuous. Again, this conflicts with what one may think of as an entirely reasonable concept image of continuity, and when "strange examples" are introduced, the tension between a concept image and the extension of a formal definition can lead students to experience confusion and distress. For some students, resolving this confusion can be valuable in leading to a better understanding of the role of formal definitions; for others, however, it may remain unresolved.

1.2.4   Developing images for new concepts: group theory

Many of the examples we've given so far seem to suggest that the key problem arises when a concept definition is introduced long after a concept image is constructed, either because the concept has been encountered earlier, as with function and tangent, or because the language used is so evocative of imagery, as with increasing and limit. One might imagine, then, that these problems would not occur in situations where the language, the definition and the initial encounters with examples and images occur together in the teaching process.

However, Edwards & Ward (2004) addressed this issue explicitly. Group theory does, of course, have its own problems of spontaneous conceptions: the terms "set" and "group" have similar meanings outside mathematics, and students may for a time treat the idea of group as though it did just mean set without considering any extra structure (Dubinsky et al., 1994). However, Edwards and Ward found, to their surprise, that students brought all manner of inappropriate imagery to situations they had expected to be so abstract as to warrant no approach other than a definitional one. They give an example of a student who was asked to calculate cosets. She was provided with the definition, but rather than use this, she struggled for twenty minutes to remember what she had done previously. They also found that for others, working with the coset product brought to mind imagery based on earlier experiences with multiplication such as the distributive property of multiplying two binomials ("first-outer-inner-last"), or set operations such as taking the union.

1.2.5 Complicated definitions: convergence

Before we conclude this section, we discuss one more point about learning to work with definitions. In all of the above sections, we have discussed ways in which a concept image, pre-existing or built up from new experience, may pull students towards an interpretation of a concept that is incorrect relative to the corresponding formal definition. Here we note that there is often a simultaneous push effect causing students to actively avoid consulting definitions: definitions are often complicated!

A feeling for this can be generated by considering the following statements:

> For every tire in the library, there is a car in the
> parking lot such that if the tire fits the car, then the
> car is red.
>
> Amongst all the fish flying around the gymnasium,
> there is one for which there is, in every Computer
> Science class, a Physics major who knows how much
> the fish weighs. (Dubinsky et al., 1988)

One may, however, note that these each contain alternating universal and existential quantifiers and are thus similar in logical structure to the definitions of sequence convergence or function continuity in real analysis. Successful mathematicians are able to think about those definitions with very little effort, because they have worked with them a lot and developed an understanding of them that is closely related to their images, appropriate examples etc. For students meeting them for the first time, however, there is a lot of work to do to get to that point, and there may be little incentive to put in this work when an existing concept image gives one the feeling that the concept is already well understood.

Some mathematicians may think these are pointless manufactured examples, with no relevance; we contend, however, that students may think exactly the same of similarly complicated mathematical definitions.

1.3 Responses: Addressing these issues

In the preceding sections we considered the following phenomena related to students' use of concept definitions:

- Pre-existing concept images might override or interfere with the use of the definition, even when the latter is known;

- Spontaneous conceptions might occur in situations in which everyday words are used in a technical context;

- Consequences of definitions might conflict directly with sensible concept images built from either previous experience or spontaneous conceptions;

- Even in situations in which a definition is introduced before any experience with the concept, students might still more or less ignore it and base their learning primarily on examples;

- Definitions themselves may be complicated and considerably harder to work with than familiar concept images.

In addressing all of these, we believe that there are two major problems to be considered. The primary one, which we address here, is that students are not aware that definitions have a special status in advanced mathematics, so that when they encounter them they do not use them as they should. That is, they often make judgements on the basis of comparisons with concept images and treat mathematical definitions as, at best, dictionary-style descriptions or, at worst, irrelevant. The second problem, which we will address more fully in Chapter 3, is that the concept image and definition may fail to coincide significantly: clearly many mathematicians rely on their images to make judgements in thinking mathematically, but they do so with sophisticated images which they can rely on to closely match the definition.

The first problem – of simply not using definitions mathematically – seems like it should have a simple solution, but of course it doesn't. First, as Davis and Vinner point out, existing conceptions don't go away when we learn something new, and "the presentation by a student of an old (and incorrect) idea cannot be taken as evidence that the student does not know the correct idea. In many cases the student knows both, but has retrieved the old idea" (Davis & Vinner, 1986, p.284). Nor does the presentation of a correct definition indicate that a student will necessarily use this appropriately in any given situation. As Vinner notes, one of the things that might happen when a student learns a definition is that this is memorised but remains essentially separate from the rest of the concept image, so that (in the context of learning about general co-ordinate systems), "the moment the student is asked to define a co-ordinate system he will repeat his or her teacher's definition, but in all other situations he or she will think of a co-ordinate system as a configuration of two perpendicular axes" (Vinner, 1991, p.70).

Moreover, we do not want students to abandon their concept images, or to avoid having any spontaneous conceptions. Some of the world's best mathematicians emphasise the importance of intuition, examples, mental models etc. in mathematical thinking (e.g. Poincaré, 1913; Thurston, 1994). What we want is for our students to learn to evoke the definitions when appropriate. Given that this has rarely if ever been systematically required before, it will probably take them some time to acquire the discipline to do it.

Learning is a complex process, and learning to relate new definitions to existing concept images is necessarily going to be far from straightforward. As Davis and Vinner put it,

> Even if words and ideas from outside of mathematics could be excluded from a student's concept image, and if one could work entirely within mathematics, it would still be necessary for each student to build mental representations gradually. One cannot put anything as complex as limit into a single idea that can appear instantaneously in complete and mature form. (Davis & Vinner, 1986, p.300)

So learning to use definitions appropriately is not likely to be something that a student can master overnight, no matter how good our teaching. Nonetheless, for us, awareness of this underlying problem has a large impact on how we think about our own teaching. There are many small-scale, day-to-day activities that we engage in to address it, the principal ones of which are outlined below.

1. *Explaining the problem.* The most obvious thing we do is to tell students about the issue – that is, explain carefully and repeatedly that when mathematicians give a definition, they really mean it; that definitions have a special status in advanced mathematics and that this is different from the status of dictionary definitions in everyday life (Edwards & Ward (2004) suggested using Vinner's 1991 diagrams as part of this discussion). In giving such explanations we try to get across the three basic points of

a definition: everything which has the properties of the definition is an instance of the concept, everything which is an instance of the concept has the defining properties, and that this is useful because everything deduced from the definition applies to all instances of the concept.

2. *Acknowledging counterintuitive aspects.* We take particular care to highlight instances in which the formal definition may include or exclude elements (or even whole subclasses) in a way that might seem counterintuitive relative to a concept image. We thus repeatedly emphasise that the use of a word in everyday speech may depend on the context and that in mathematics, definitions give words very precise meanings. When doing so, however, we take care to acknowledge that some uses of terms might seem strange at first, and that it is perfectly fine to feel a bit uncomfortable about this. We stress this because we do not want our students to begin thinking that mathematics is simply a formal game in which there are no sensible meanings.

3. *Highlighting use of definitions in context.* We tend to emphasise the use of definitions in proofs, in order for students to be able to see the way that definitions enable us to deduce new properties which apply to every instance of the concept. For instance, when a proof aims to show that a definition is satisfied, this may be obvious to someone who already has a mathematical notion of definition, but it could be valuable to students to point out exactly where the statements of definitions appear within proofs,

and how the statement of the definition often dictates the structure of the proof.

4. *Testing knowledge of definitions.* We sometimes use regular tests of definitions as part of assessment. This can be contentious because we do not want to encourage rote memorisation, and obviously we would be delighted if students developed a full understanding of the meanings of definitions as they went along. However, this is unlikely and in the meantime students need to be able to recognise definitions when they are used and to write them down accurately at will. If they are not able to reproduce or even recognise a given definition, they will have failed at the first hurdle; it may be useful to contemplate what a set of analysis lecture notes must look like if one has not managed this. Of course, regular tests also send the message that we think that definitions are important.

5. *Paying attention to the examples used.* If every function a student sees is continuous, they are likely to incorporate continuity as part of their concept image of function. If every sequence they see is monotonic, they are likely to think primarily of monotonic sequences when reasoning about sequences in general. For this reason, we try to be careful with the examples we give and the sketches that we draw, to highlight variation and to avoid routinely incorporating non-essential properties. This is not always easy as certain key or favourite examples will tend to come up again and again. In some cases there is a good reason for this, but in these cases we try to be aware that we are

probably inducing an inappropriate concept image in at least some of our students.

Each of these five things can be incorporated routinely into standard lectures. Most lecturers probably do them to some extent anyway, although perhaps not very systematically. We now do them a lot, and have long since stopped worrying that students would find this patronising. It is important to remember that when they arrive at university, students genuinely do not know that *show that every convergent sequence is bounded* means *show that a general sequence that satisfies the definition of convergent also satisfies the definition of bounded* (Alcock & Simpson, 2002). They are usually grateful for the help in recognising structure at this level.

As well as these day-to-day activities and emphases, there are also larger scale things that can be tried in order to help students to develop a mathematical view of definitions. Some of these are quite drastic; both mathematicians and mathematics educators have experimented with reconfiguring entire courses so that they adopt a "guided rediscovery" approach in which students begin by experimenting with particular structures and gradually, with the help of a teacher, refine their ideas into formal definitions, theorems and proofs (e.g. Yackel et al., 2000; Zandieh et al., 2008).

The aim of such an approach is to give students access to more authentic mathematical experience. In particular, it can allow students to experience a negotiation between examples and definitions in which definitions might change to better capture the boundaries suggested by examples (like that described in historical context by Lakatos, 1976). Undergraduate mathematics students are not normally party to this process, so an approach like this should, in theory, make the definitions chosen seem more meaningful and less arbitrary. Even in small-class situations in which this is viable, however, it may not provide a complete solution; Davis & Vinner (1986) report a case in which a small class of high-achieving high school students attended a specialist course based on this principle, which was considered successful in its learning goals at the time but which did not lead to retention of the formal definitions over a break (of course, this does not detract from the fact that the students may well have learned a great deal about mathematical reasoning by being involved).

Another approach, which lends itself better to smaller-scale implementation within a standard lecture course, is to increase the number and range of examples considered. Many presentations in textbooks introduce a definition and give only one or two examples, perhaps with a non-example. The assumption seems to be that students will somehow get a sense of the whole concept by seeing these examples as generic and/or by recognising the significance of the non-example in highlighting the concept's boundaries. Hopefully the above discussion has convinced you that for many students, this is unlikely to result in a concept image that is fully compatible with the range of variation permitted by the definition. Our own teaching now tends to include more tasks that address a range of examples, with a deliberate attempt to convey a sense of the range of variation that is possible within a concept. In this we very much follow Watson & Mason (2005), who have written extensively on the development of conceptual understanding through the use of tasks which require students to give examples. Illustrations of this are given in Chapter 3.

We have also tried example classification tasks, in two different formats. In introducing the definitions of open, closed and limit points for sets, we set a task in which students had to work in groups to decide which of a list of subsets of the reals satisfied each definition. It took the students much longer than expected to work out how to apply these quantified statements to the sets in question; as ever such an experience was both somewhat alarming and illuminating. In the second format, we tried asking students to make their own classifications before introducing definitions. This, obviously, does not work for terms like open and closed sets that have no obvious meaning, but it is easily applied for concepts like increasing. Taking this approach allows for the possibility for uncertainty and disagreement, for which the definition can be introduced as a resolution: an answer to a problem rather than an arbitrary starting point for a new topic.

The use of such example-based tasks brings us back to the subtleties we described earlier, however. On the one hand we might try to help students develop their concept image to a point at which it is compatible with the formal definition and is unlikely to lead them astray in their reasoning. On the other hand, we want them to understand that they should be focussing less on their concept image and learning to work in a disciplined way with formal definitions. As ever, individual teachers will take different approaches to addressing this dilemma, but by recognising the underlying problem we can better understand our students' behaviour, and at least take steps to address it.

Chapter 2

Mathematical objects

2.1 Introduction

Consider the expression $3 + 2$. This piece of symbolism can be thought of as having a dual nature. It represents both a process (adding the two numbers) and the result of that process (the sum) (Gray & Tall, 1994). Mathematics is replete with similar cases in which a concept can be thought of as an object or a process depending upon the context. William Thurston described his discovery of another elementary case like this:

> I remember as a child, in fifth grade, coming to the amazing (to me) realization that the answer to 134 divided by 29 is $\frac{134}{29}$ (and so forth). What a tremendous labor-saving device! To me, "134 divided by

29" meant a certain tedious chore, while $\frac{134}{29}$ was an object with no implicit work. I went excitedly to my father to explain my major discovery. He told me that of course this is so, $\frac{a}{b}$ and a divided by b are just synonyms. To him it was just a small variation in notation. (Thurston, 1990)

Gray & Tall (1994) list many more examples, among them:

- The symbol $+4$ stands for both the process of "add 4"' or shift four units along the number line, and the concept of the positive number $+4$.

- The function notation $f(x) = x^2 - 3$ simultaneously tells both how to calculate the value of the function for a particular value of x and encapsulates the complete concept of the function for a general value of x.

- The notation $\lim_{x \to a} f(x)$ represents both the process of tending to a limit and the concept of the value of the limit, as do $\lim_{n \to \infty} s_n$, $\lim_{n \to \infty} \sum_{k=1}^{n} a_k$. (Gray & Tall, 1994, p.120)

They argue that the ability to interpret ambiguous symbols in this flexible way is at the root of successful mathematical thinking. This is powerfully illustrated by considering what elementary arithmetic looks like if you interpret numbers only as instructions to perform the process of counting. If 3 is an instruction to count to 3, and 5 is an instruction to count to 5, this leads to the quite complicated "super-process" for $3+5$ of counting to 3, counting to 5 and then putting all these items together and counting them all. Indeed, this "count-all" strategy is well-recognised in literature on early arithmetic. More sophisticated strategies are "count-on", "count-on from larger", and students might eventually learn some sums as "known facts" and be able to use these to generate more "derived facts" (Secada, Fuson and Hall, 1983). This sequence is a caricature of any particular individual's development of early arithmetic (for example, many children will pick up some "known facts" before learning to count-on), and not all students will move along this sequence at the same pace. Gray and Tall found that:

> We see that the [age] 10+ below–average group, sometimes known as slow learners in the UK, appear to possess the same profile as the 8+ above–average group, but they do not use these facts in the same way. The above average 8+ derive most facts that they do not know; the below average 10+ children derive no facts [for certain problems] ... Instead they count. We suggest that the phrase "slow learners" is therefore a misnomer. The less able do not simply learn the same techniques more slowly. They develop different techniques. (Gray & Tall, 1994, p.129)

If a student is primarily counting instead of co-ordinating facts, imagine how difficult it must be to perform calculations like $13 + 15$, 3×5, $15 - 13$ etc. This might seem far removed from university level, but in fact similar effects appear throughout mathematics, including (as we will see) with concepts such as function and coset. Students may experience a sensation of not understanding the mathematics because, where we see a simple object that has to be manipulated in some way, they might see a long process that it just too big and messy to think about as a whole.

2.2   Process-object theories

Process-object theories, as they are often called, have been used to account for a wide range of student difficulties, and in this section we consider how they apply to various specific mathematical concepts including functions, cosets and series. The first of these topics receives longer treatment as we use it to introduce more fully some ideas and terminology from the mathematics education literature about this issue. The remaining topics each highlight some particular issue in thinking about mathematical constructs as objects. Finally, as in Chapter 1, we offer some comments about how we and others as teachers are influenced by conceptualising students' difficulties in this way.

2.2.1   Moving from a process to an object conception: functions

As mathematicians, we can think of a function as a process that takes some input and gives an output. We can also think of a function as an object that can itself be an input to a higher level process, like differentiation, or speak of general functions f and g and make meaning of expressions like $f + g$ without considering any particular functions. We can do this because we have been thinking about functions for a long time, but our initial experience may have been quite different. Early experience with functions (occurring at the age of around 11 [Key Stage 3] in the UK) may have required simply evaluating an expression for various values of the argument. If students are able to do this but are unable to do very much else, they are said by Dubinsky and his colleagues to have an *action* conception of function (Asiala et al., 1996; Cottrill et al., 1996). This action conception is the first stage of the APOS theory, in which conceptions are described as passing through phases of Action, Process, Object and Schema.

These authors described the way in which the individual gradually increases their control over such an action until they can think of it as a *process* where they can describe, or reflect on, all the steps in the action without necessarily performing them (Cottrill et al., 1996; Dubinsky & Harel, 1992). In the case of function, an individual would be said to have a process conception if they can imagine reversing the process to obtain inverse functions, or linking two or more processes to compose functions. Dubinsky (1991) also argued that this level of conceptualization is necessary for fully making sense of graphing or whether a function is surjective or injective.

Finally, further experience and reflection lead via encapsulation to an object conception. This encapsulation is achieved when the individual becomes aware of the totality of the process, realises that transformations can act on it, and is able to construct such transformations (Cottrill et al., 1996). An object conception of function is necessary in order to make full sense of higher level operations that take functions as inputs and return them as outputs. Differentiation and integration are classic examples here: each takes functions as inputs and returns them as outputs. If one is not able to think of functions as objects, this is likely to make little sense (though, of course, one may still be able to learn routines of symbol manipulation).

Three issues can further complicate the situation.

First, in many mathematical situations there is a requirement to combine processes and objects at multiple levels, for which it helps to be able to keep track of "what kind of thing" everything is. For instance, as a process, the expression

$$\frac{d}{dx}(4x^2 + 3)\Big|_{x=2}$$

requires differentiating a function (here inputs and outputs are both functions) and then evaluating the result at a certain point (inputs and outputs are both numbers). As an object, therefore, the expression $\frac{d}{dx}(4x^2 + 3)\big|_{x=2}$ "is" a number. A mathematically sophisticated person would have no problem asserting this. However, the expression certainly doesn't look like a number, so a relatively inexperienced student might only be able to assert that it is one after going through a long process of evaluation. Again, this makes it clear how powerful an object conception is. To complicate matters, sometimes when we write numbers in function contexts, we are actually treating them as functions. When we apply the sum rule to differentiate $f + 1$ we are really treating the "1" as a constant function rather than a number. This doesn't seem to be particularly problematic in this case, but we have certainly seen students become confused by the idea that we can apply the sum rule for limits to the sequence $(a_n + 1)$, because "1 is not a sequence". It is particularly useful to be able to keep track of the object in situations in which two expressions are notationally very similar: $\int_0^1 (4x^2 + 3)\, dx$ is a number, but $\int (4x^2 + 3)\, dx$ is a family of functions. Again this is a possible source of student confusion. Most students, at some point, have probably treated all of these expressions as instructions to perform sequences of algebraic actions, and for a time it may seem entirely mysterious that as answers one sometimes gets numbers and sometimes gets functions.

Second, we have primarily been discussing functions that take numbers as inputs, but in many cases students have to deal with functions that operate on other kinds of object. These underlying objects may themselves not be well encapsulated. Consider, for example, trigonometric functions like $\sin(x)$. In one sense, these take angles as inputs and return numbers which are calculated from ratios. Both may be thought of as numbers, of course, but we speculate that for many students, the process of drawing a right-angled triangle with the appropriate angle, measuring selected sides and finding their ratio may be less amenable to encapsulation than a process like "double the number and add 2". Students who have not managed this encapsulation will struggle to make any meaningful sense of the idea of differentiating $\sin(x)$. Our notational conventions add to the ambiguity by making it hard to distinguish the number $x^3 + 4$ (for a given x) and the function $x^3 + 4$ (standing for "cube and add 4"), in contrast to the distinction between the function $\sin$ and the value $\sin(x)$ or the function f and the value $f(x)$.

Third, in advanced mathematics we often talk about functions without invoking specific functions at all. We write sentences about f and g and everyone is supposed to be able to imagine that these represent general functions, possibly from some restricted set as specified by particular properties. As discussed in Chapter 1, it may be that the range of examples of which a student has experience is considerably impoverished compared with our own, and that faced with such sentences some students don't think of illustrative examples at all (Dahlberg & Housman, 1997). We will discuss some implications of this point for constructing and understanding proofs in Chapter 3.

2.2.2 A quicker process-object development: cosets

In the case of function, students have somewhere in the region of seven years for development from an action through a process to an object conception before they begin to use the concept at university. This is significant because, as Sfard (1991) points out, a great deal of time might be necessary to move from an action conception to an object conception; further, she argues, one may need to see higher level actions on putative objects in order to begin to see those things *as* objects.

For many other concepts at the university level, a similar development is necessary, but a much shorter time period is available. In this section we consider one of these, the concept of coset.

Students are typically introduced to the notion of a coset

in a first course on group theory. Their first experience with
the concept is likely to involve calculating specific cosets in
the context of specific groups. They thus have the opportunity
to perform transformations involving specific elements, and we
might expect that they will initially treat these transformations
as externally directed actions in Dubinsky's sense. We hope,
however, that they will quite rapidly interiorise the process of
finding cosets and be able to imagine doing so without having to
actually do all the calculations. This is probably not unreason-
able given that the students have progressed to this level, even
though we probably give fewer examples than students have
been accustomed to in school, both in our own presentations
and in the problems we assign for them to do. So far, this is
similar to the development of the function concept.

However, there is far less time for students to reach an object conception for coset. Where students have years to learn
to treat functions as objects, in the case of the coset concept,
they may well have less than a week. It may be that the coset
concept is introduced with illustrative calculations, and only a
couple of lectures later cosets are being treated as objects that
can be counted, compared, multiplied together and that may
themselves be members of groups. Students might be required,
for instance, to work with $H = \{0, 4, 8, 12, 16\}$ as a subgroup of
the $(\mathbb{Z}_{20}, +)$, and to interpret the symbol $2 + H$ as an object
in order to use it in calculations like $(1 + H) + (2 + H)$. A
mathematician would have no problem with this, and would be
able to move flexibly between thinking of the "answer" as the
unified object $3 + H$ or (if required) as the process of adding
3 (mod 20) to each element of H. For a student, however, the

symbol $2 + H$ might signify only the process of calculating. As such, the expression $(1 + H) + (2 + H)$ might seem to involve a long co-ordination of processes rather than a simple addition of objects (Dubinsky et al., 1994). Other notations, such as $[g_1][g_2] = [g_1 g_2]$ may make it easier to treat cosets in calculations as objects by obscuring the underlying processes. However, while this notational sleight of hand may allow students to progress, it does not necessarily mean they have connected the processes to the objects.

The three issues we outlined in the preceding section on functions can further complicate things in the case of cosets, too.

First, again one is frequently in a situation in which different types of processes and objects are involved, and it may be important to keep track of what kind of thing everything is. For instance, one might want students to consider the group D_3 (the symmetries of an equilateral triangle), H as the subgroup formed by the rotations and r_1 as one of the reflections, and to ask whether $r_1 H = H r_1$. This could involve the following:

- a triangle as a basic object;

- symmetries which can be thought of as processes ("turn it over" etc.) but need to be thought of as objects that can be elements of sets and that can be combined;

- the group D_3 as a special kind of set of these symmetries, which has internal structure provided by the process of composition that acts on the symmetries;

- the subgroup H as a subset of this set, which also has internal structure provided by the same process of composition that acts on the symmetries;

- the cosets $r_1 H$ and $H r_1$, which can be thought of as processes but need to be compared as objects that are equal or not.

The question is about whether two cosets are equal, but there are a number of different processes and objects that must be combined and compared in order to answer this.

A second issue is that the group elements themselves may not be well encapsulated. Numbers are very familiar so that at least calculating cosets in groups of integers involves operations on familiar objects. Other objects, such as permutations or symmetries, are probably not familiar and may themselves be unencapsulated processes for many students; we are asking them to treat a *transformation* as an object, rather than thinking about the *thing that is being transformed* as the object. It isn't hard to see that considerable mental discipline might be required to do this, since "the transposition of 1 and 2" is less "objecty" than 1 and 2, and "rotate through $120°$" is certainly less "objecty" than a cardboard cut-out triangle. Of course, the whole point of abstract algebra is that we can identify commonalities across ostensibly very different types of structure. But it may be difficult for a student to appreciate this if it means trying to compare things that feel like objects in one area with things that feel like actions or processes in another.

Third, once again mathematics at this level involves lots of general theorems about relationships between classes of mathematical objects. For instance, the sentence

> The map $\phi_g : H \longrightarrow gH$ defined by $\phi_g(h) = gh$ is a bijection

is about the map and treats it as a noun. For a student "a map" might not be the kind of thing that could be described using a noun, so that the sentence seems more likely to be "about" group elements in some vague and confusing way. It might also be illuminating to think about how much sense a student could possibly make of this if they think of gH only as a process.

2.2.3   Keeping track of the objects: series convergence

In the cases of functions and cosets we have emphasised the point that mathematical situations can involve numerous different types of processes and objects. In this section we offer a more detailed illustration of the potential difficulty of keeping track of "what kind of thing" each object is in such a situation. For this we use the example of the concept of radius of convergence of a power series and the process of finding a radius of convergence using the ratio test. In our experience, lecturers tend to think that using the ratio test is a straightforward process, but students find the whole business very confusing. One reason for this may be the number and nature of the processes and objects involved.

Consider the apparently straightforward question: Find the radius of convergence of the power series $\sum_{n=0}^{\infty} \frac{nx^n}{2^n+1}$.

A power series such as this can be thought of as a *function* of x, which for each *number* x gives a *series* (so there are infinitely many series under consideration). Each series may add up to a *number* (that's two numbers so far) or it may not. For this type of question, we do not actually care what this second number is, just whether there is one or not. Instead, we care about the *set* of all numbers x for which the series does add up to some number. This set is also, apparently, an interval which is centred at 0 and so will be specified by a third *number*, often called R, the radius of convergence (which, if you are just working with real numbers, doesn't seem related to circles). We use the ratio test to find this number R. We do this by taking general consecutive terms of the series, each of which is represented by an *expression* in x and n (n represents a fourth *number*). We find the quotient of these expressions and treat this as another single *expression* (that's two expressions in x and n so far). We then temporarily ignore the fact that x is a variable, and treat this second expression as a *sequence* indexed by n. We find the limit of the sequence, which will be a third *expression*, though just in x and not n (which may well nonetheless be unexpected, because limits have usually been numbers). We then go back to treating x as a variable, to ask for which values of x the modulus of this expression is less than 1. This answer to this will be the set of numbers we described above, of the form $\{x : |x| < R\}$. This number R is the answer to the original question.

Superficially, using the ratio test to find a radius of convergence is a simple algebraic procedure. Thinking of it in the above terms, however, makes it clear just how many different objects of different types are involved. Our description involved, at least:

- one function;

- infinitely many series;

- four numbers, of which

    - one we don't care about;

    - two are general and represented by letters;

    - one is the one we're actually trying to find;

- one set of numbers;

- three expressions in x (one of the general numbers), of which

    - two also involve n (the other general number);

    - one is treated as a sequence;

    - one is the limit of that sequence;

Understanding this complicated construction may be further confounded by the fact that a student may see a series as an unencapsulated process of adding more and more terms. Such a student may be unable to think about any individual series as actually equal to a number, let alone to imagine iterating across infinitely many different series and asking for each one whether it is equal to a number or not. Even a student who can competently perform the required manipulations might lose track of what they are actually accomplishing, and be very unclear about what they have found or achieved by the time they get to the end of the process (try finding a student who can reliably apply the ratio test in radius of convergence problems and asking them what the number at the end tells us).

Note that nothing in our description even begins to address *why* the ratio test works!

2.2.4 What kind of object might have that property?

The above discussions hopefully make it clear that where a mathematician might look at a piece of notation and see an object that, if appropriate, can be de-encapsulated into a process, a student might see just the process or even individual actions that compose that process. Hence, where a mathematician might experience a simple, neat and tidy network of relationships among two or three concepts, a student might experience a complicated mass of long-winded processes that are somehow related to each other in ways that are difficult to pin down. This underlying confusion can manifest itself in a number of ways.

First, students who can carry out some process are often unable to articulate what it is that this process achieves or why what they have found by the end of it is a reasonable answer to the question. This phenomenon is invisible in written responses, but when teaching small groups of students it can be very illuminating to ask them to try to explain how the process and outcome are related. In one of our recent tutorials, students had been asked to find bases of the kernel and image of ϕ, where $\phi : \mathbb{R}^5 \longrightarrow \mathbb{R}^4$ is given by

$$\phi \begin{pmatrix} x_1 \\ x_2 \\ x_3 \\ x_4 \\ x_5 \end{pmatrix} = \begin{pmatrix} x_1 - x_2 - x_3 \\ x_1 + 3x_4 - x_5 \\ x_2 - x_3 + 2x_4 + x_5 \\ -x_3 - x_4 + x_5 \end{pmatrix}$$

Most of the small group had attempted this and (aided by a similar example in their notes) had made some progress. However, some of their answers made no sense, containing vectors with the wrong number of components, or being given as something other than vectors altogether – numbers, commonly, in some sort of confusion with the dimension of the kernel. When asked "What kind of thing is the kernel of phi?" they were largely unable to respond, though through more specific questions about the possibilities ("Is it a number?", "Is it a vector?", "Is it just one vector or more than one?") we were able to converge on the sensible answer "It's a set of vectors" and additionally specify bounds on how many vectors a basis for it might contain. But it was clear that the students had never thought about their answers in these terms before.

Similar difficulties appear in the case of relations. In our experience, many students will be able to do some manipulations with inequalities and state something like "it is transitive" but be totally unable to say what "it" is. This is hardly surprising: even from our standpoint as people who can discipline ourselves to think of a relation as an object that have certain properties or not, "less than or equal to" still seems like a pretty bizarre thing to treat as a 'thing'.

Second, when students do manage to talk about mathematics in terms of its objects, they may attach properties to the wrong kinds of objects. Alcock (2008) quoted a mathematician lamenting this phenomenon:

> I'd like to call it... an "error of category". One of my favorite example of this, ... when I'd asked "prove that the intersection of two compact sets is compact"... [the response was] "Let A and B be compact sets... then every point in A is compact, and every point in B is compact, and therefore...." Okay. So, and those kinds of mistakes, particularly among the weaker students, are pretty common. I mean, [...] they don't even understand the nature of the objects they're dealing with.

Similar instances of "category errors" that we have come across in research and teaching include:

- thinking that in the set of vectors

$$\left\{ \begin{pmatrix} 1 \\ 0 \end{pmatrix}, \begin{pmatrix} 0 \\ 1 \end{pmatrix}, \begin{pmatrix} 1 \\ 1 \end{pmatrix} \right\},$$

  the first two are linearly independent and the third is linearly dependent;

- thinking that in a sequence with a graph like that in Figure 2.1, the terms beyond N do converge but the earlier terms don't;

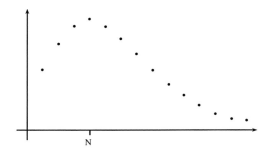

N

Figure 2.1: Convergent/non-convergent sequence

- Thinking that the set $\{4, \{-3, 2, -1/7\}, \{\{17, 5\}\}\}$ has six elements rather than three (Dubinsky, 1991).

Some of this confusion may be about discipline in using new language, but it is probably not a coincidence that all of these cases seem to involve attaching the property word to objects that are more familiar to the student than those "one level up" where the word really should be attached: here *convergent* is applied to the numbers in the sequence, not to the sequence of numbers, *linearly independent* is applied to vectors not to sets of vectors, and *membership* is applied to familiar base objects (numbers), not sets of objects.

Third, sometimes properties that have originally applied to a particular object are detached and applied to a new situation in which some other object has this property but the original one doesn't. This may not be clear to students. Working with the same tutorial group as above, we saw an instance of this in which the students had been asked to show that $\mathbb{R}^2$, with scalar multiplication defined as usual, but addition defined by

$$(u_1, u_2) + (v_1, v_2) = (u_1 + v_1 + 2, u_2 + v_2 + 2),$$

was not a real vector space. The students were just getting to grips with the definition of vector space, and were excited to think that they had solved the problem by noticing that adding $(0,0)$ to a vector (u_1, u_2) did not leave the vector unchanged, so that the additive identity requirement was not satisfied. At this point, Lara found herself reluctantly having to say, "Ah, well, *zero* is not the zero...," and was not surprised that the students seemed horrified by the degree to which the mathematical ground was apparently moving under their feet.

2.3 Responses: Addressing these issues

In the preceding sections we considered the following phenomena related to whether or not a student can think of a mathematical construct as an object:

- Higher level processes may not make much sense unless one can think of lower level constructs as objects;

- University-level syllabuses might demand very quick encapsulations of processes into objects;

- Mathematical situations often involve a variety of processes and objects at different levels, and keeping track of what kind of thing everything is can be difficult;

- Students sometimes seem to attach properties to objects at the wrong level.

Once again, recognising that the "objects problem" is an issue that students face helps us to make sense of their difficulties, and to have a better sense of how the world of mathematics might look through their eyes. As with the concept image/concept definition distinction, we find this conceptualization of particular help because the phenomenon is so pervasive – a great many of the major recognised sticking points for students can be identified as ones in which it is necessary to encapsulate a process and treat the result as an object. This helps us to see one major class of problems rather than hundreds of separate difficulties. Of course, as in the previous chapter, seeing things in this way does not provide us with a way to avoid the difficulties or with an instant solution: we cannot "give" a student an object conception. But it does mean that we can begin to think about types of explanation and tasks that might help students to improve their understanding. We again consider both small-scale and large-scale possible responses.

First, on a day-to-day scale, we again find that there are several things we do in lectures that address this issue directly:

1. *Pointing out what the objects are.* We tend to make a point of highlighting the situations in which constructs are

treated as objects, saying things like "Now we are thinking of these sets (etc.) as objects in their own right", "We treat this symmetry as an object that can be a member of a set" and so on. This can even be done systematically, by taking a mathematical question that is about several different kinds of object, such as "let $\phi : H \rightarrow gH$ be defined by $\phi(h) = gh$, prove that $|H| = |gH|$", and identifying them all: "ϕ is a map, g is a group element, H is a subgroup of G, gH is a coset" etc. [1]

2. *Asking "what kind of thing is...?" questions.* We also find ourselves regularly asking students to make this identification, particularly in abstract topics such as abstract and linear algebra. The archetype of this is "What kind of thing is the kernel of phi?" It is often difficult for students to answer these questions, as they have often never thought about mathematics in this way before. But they do seem to get the hang of it relatively quickly.

3. *Asking whether sentences make sense.* When encountering new mathematical objects, we find it useful to spend some time looking at what one can do with them and whether their appearance in mathematical-looking expressions make sense. For a simple example, if A and B are sets of natural numbers and m and n are natural numbers, which of the following might make sense:

---

[1] We are indebted to Jean Flower for this suggestion.

(a) $A \cap n$	(b) $n + m$	(c) $n + A$	(d) $A + B$
(e) $\{n\} \cup A$	(f) $n \times m$	(g) $A \times B$	(h) $n \times \lvert A \rvert$
(i) $-- n$	(j) $-- A$	(k) A^c	(l) n^c

In some of these, like (a), there is no accessible and sensible way in which they might make sense; in others, like (b), (c) and (d), one could make sense of this but only if the symbol "+" has subtly different meanings. This kind of activity may again encourage students to attend very carefully to what kind of object something is and what kind of processes can act upon that object.

4. *Attending to the development of underlying concepts.* We try to notice cases in which students may not have a good enough sense of old concepts to make sense of new material. For instance, students often do not seem to have the experience of taking a power series and adding together the first few terms for different values of x. Having them do this can give at least some the sense that different things happen for different values of x and that this is therefore worth investigating. This is not unproblematic, of course, because we do not wish to give students the idea that adding together a few terms is enough, but feel that, on balance, they might benefit.

On a larger scale, researchers have designed teaching sequences around a breakdown of constructions that a student would need to make in order to understand a topic area. Dubinsky and his colleagues referred to this breakdown as a genetic decomposition, which is described by Asiala et al. (1996) as "a structured set of mental constructs which might describe how the concept can develop in the mind of an individual". They have developed instructional sequences for mathematical induction (Dubinsky, 1987; Dubinsky, 1989), quantification (Dubinsky et al., 1988), and function (Dubinsky & Harel, 1992; Breidenbach et al., 1992). These instructional sequences often involve both computer programming in the language ISETL which uses very mathematical-like constructs (including the ability to define functions which can then be passed, as objects, to be acted on by other functions) and social interaction among students, which they cite as promoting reflection.

This approach relies on the belief that the developmental sequence followed by individuals is a process-object sequence. Both Dubinsky (1991) and Sfard (1991) treated it as such, and there are good reasons to think of it this way. Certainly this is consistent with much of our teaching sequences as well as with much historical development.

Clearly, however, this is not a complete description of cognitive development (Slavitt, 1997). Sfard (1991) herself suggested that certain types of representation, particularly graphical, facilitate an object conception of function, and Slavitt described a property-oriented view in which functions come to be conceived as objects possessing local and global properties such as intercepts, symmetry and asymptotes. Also, the mathematical sentences and expressions students encounter have objects and processes indicated by their grammatical or syntactic status. We would contend that, if students can get used to manipulating them within grammatically (and mathematically) correct rules, they may simply come to see things which appear as nouns as objects. Thus it may be that students can to some extent by-pass the "objects" problem by letting the symbols do the work, in the sense Weyl (1940) described. This in itself raises issues of how students attend to symbols and words, and these will be further addressed in the next chapter.

CHAPTER 3

Two reasoning strategies

3.1 Introduction

In the previous two chapters, we discussed difficulties students face with learning advanced mathematics. In these cases, students need to develop certain ways of thinking: they *must* get used to working mathematically with definitions in making classifications and as the basis for deductions; they *must* think about certain constructs as objects if they are to make full sense of more complicated or abstract structures. In these respects there is, crudely, a *right* way of thinking to aim for.

This chapter is different; it suggests that there are two equally viable and sensible approaches to thinking about mathematical statements and proofs, and that while we probably all use both approaches to some extent, some of us tend to favour one over the other. Hence in this chapter we make a distinction within mathematical practice, but not one which is a blunt right/wrong or better/worse distinction between novice and more expert mathematical thinkers.

In this chapter we focus particularly on proof *construction*, but note that when we talk of "proof" we think of this as including many related, but different activities, such as: constructing a proof, reading a proof for correctness, reading a proof for understanding, producing a counter-example, determining truth/falsity of a statement. Much of what we discuss below applies to these activities too.

3.2   Two strategies

We introduce this distinction by contrasting the responses of two undergraduate students to a task presented in a research interview. The two students, Brad and Carla, were both successful students enrolled in a "transition to proof" course at a respected US institution (Alcock & Weber, 2008). You may like to read the task first and pay attention to your own thinking as you first respond to it.

Definitions

A function $f : \mathbb{R} \longrightarrow \mathbb{R}$ is said to be **increasing** if for all $x, y \in \mathbb{R}$, $(x > y$ implies $f(x) > f(y))$.

A function $f : \mathbb{R} \longrightarrow \mathbb{R}$ is said to **have a global maximum at a real number c** if for all $x \in \mathbb{R}$ such that $x \neq c$, $f(x) < f(c)$.

Task

Suppose f is an increasing function. Prove that there is no real number c that is a global maximum for f.

We describe Brad's approach and then Carla's.

Brad commented that he was trying to understand the question and then stated,

B: And I'm going to take an example to make sure I'm doing it right.

He wrote the following on his paper, along with a small sketch graph of $f(x) = x$:

$$f(x) = x \qquad x = 2 \ \ f(2) = 2 \qquad y = 3 \ \ f(3) = 3$$

He wondered, "can f of c be repeated?" and sketched a sine curve with two local maxima marked, before rejecting this idea. He then talked quietly to himself for a moment before suggesting an overall proof tactic.

B: I think we can do this by contradiction. Assume that ... assume that um ... if f is an increasing function then c ... then there is ... a c? For which there is a max. And then prove that that can't happen. And then, so that'll prove it.

He began to work on this idea, but found it difficult to make progress. After he had struggled for some time and reconsidered his graph, he appeared ready to give up, but he gave the following explanation when encouraged by the interviewer to talk through his thinking.

> B: I'm thinking that in the definition of increasing, there's never going to be one number that's the greatest. There is always going to be like, a number greater than x. Because it's, because it's increasing. So there's always going to be some number greater than the last. So if x is greater than - that's what I assumed here. x is greater than y, then there's going to be some $x + 1$, that is going to be greater than $y + 1$, so that $f(x + 1)$ is going to be greater than $f(y + 1)$. [...]. So then, there can't be some number, you know that ... if it's increasing there can't be some number that's greater than all of them. Or, some $f(c)$.

Carla's strategy was different. She read the question and then immediately began writing, saying,

> C: So ... I'm thinking the way to prove this is using contradiction. So, I would start out by assuming there exists a c for which $f(x)$ is less than $f(c)$, when x is not equal to c. Okay. *Pause.* So now I'm trying to use the definition of increasing function to prove that this cannot be. Um ... so there exists a real number for which $f(x)$ is less than $f(c)$ for all x, and there's ... f is an increasing function. For all x, y in $\mathbb{R}$, x greater than y implies $f(x)$ greater than $f(y)$. Mm.

... *pause* I guess what I'm trying to show is if x is in reals, and they are infinite ... for all x ... there will be some function $f(c)$ greater than $f(x)$. *Long pause* So there exists an element in $\mathbb{R}$ greater than c. Um ... for x ... because f is an increasing function, $f(x)$ will be greater than $f(c)$. Um ... a contradiction. So that there is no c for which $f(c)$ is greater than $f(x)$ for all x [1].

She thus constructed a correct proof. When asked about her initial strategy (to attempt proof by contradiction), Carla answered,

C: Because, in class, whenever we have some statement which says "there is... no such number," or "there exists no such number," then we assume there is, such number. And then we go on to prove that that would cause a contradiction, thus, it doesn't exist. So it was just, something ... automatically ingrained, when I see those couple of words, I think contradiction.

Unlike Brad, Carla clearly stated later that she was not referring to graphs or other representations of examples while working on this task.

I: Did you have any sort of picture in your head for this one?

---

[1] Carla's speech was slower and more hesitant than it might appear here, but minor hesitations are omitted to facilitate reading of her argument

C: No, no ...not really. I mean I know what a global maximum is from calculus .... I mean I've done these sort of things so many times. But I didn't imagine any, any sort of function. Something that would have a maximum. [...] Really ...I guess I did it very systematically and theoretically, because I just stepped this is the rule, and do it through.

We suggest that these two proof attempts can be understood as illustrations of different overall strategies for proving, as below.

When attempting to prove a mathematical statement, one sensible approach is to begin as Brad did, by considering examples of the objects to which the statement refers in order to ascertain whether the statement is true for these examples. If it does seem to be true, one might then attempt to prove it by looking for reasons why it appears to be true, perhaps by asking what relevant properties these examples all have, or perhaps by asking oneself what it would take for the statement to be false and why this is impossible. Having obtained an insight, one might then translate this into an argument framed in terms of appropriate definitions or previous theorems. We call this a *semantic* approach to proving.

An alternative sensible approach is to begin as Carla did, by writing down the definitions of the various concepts contained in the statement and using the form of the statement and/or these definitions to decide on a likely effective overall structure for the proof. One might then proceed by "unpacking" the definitions, introducing known theorems involving the relevant concepts and making logical deductions based upon any of this material, and identifying new "subgoals" in relation to finding a path of logical connections between the assumptions and the desired conclusion. This might involve general techniques such as proof by contradiction, as well as local techniques such as splitting up an expression and using the triangle inequality. We call this a *syntactic* approach to proving (Weber & Alcock, 2004). It is important to realise that describing an approach to proving as "syntactic" does not mean that it is necessarily "meaningless": one way in which people make sense of mathematical statements is through the network of links they have between symbols in a system – indeed we might argue that "semantic" and "syntactic" are just two ways of understanding "meaning" (Goldin & Kaput, 1996).

The contrast between these approaches is clear in the illustrations provided by Brad and Carla above, but of course an expert's proof attempt for a more complicated conjecture is likely to combine the two (this does not mean that all experts take the same approach; we consider the implications of this as we continue). In the next two sections we discuss in detail what it takes to use each successfully; while the above descriptions of the strategies make them sound straightforward, of course their effective application is not. In doing so we also highlight many ways in which a student might have difficulties with proof when they take a given approach. In each case we begin by discussing the strategy in relation to proof construction, though our discussion applies similarly to other proof-related activities such as understanding a proof, deciding whether a statement is true or false, and refuting a statement.

3.3   Using a semantic strategy

In order to successfully apply a semantic strategy to prove a given statement, one needs to:

1. Recognise that this strategy is applicable;

2. Have access to a suitable *example space*;

3. Be able to translate insight gained by considering examples into a general, formal proof.

3.3.1   Recognising that a semantic strategy is applicable

In order to use a semantic strategy one must first recognise that this is possible, i.e. that a statement is *about* some mathematical object(s) that can be represented in some way and that thinking about examples of such objects may help one generate a proof. This might seem like a strange thing to say, but in fact a student may not think of it that way at all, for one (or both) of these reasons:

- They might read a mathematical statement primarily for cues as to which of a range of procedures to perform.

- They might not perceive the statement as being about objects for which they could think of examples (perhaps because of the level of abstraction, as in Chapter 2).

Illustrations of the former are provided by excepts from research interviews with students taking an analysis course at a high ranking UK institution. Yvonne and Zoë were trying to answer the question: for which values of x does the series $\Sigma_{n=1}^{\infty} \frac{(-x)^n}{n}$ converge (Alcock & Simpson, 2005). They seemed to be trying to recall procedures that they had seen in lectures and ascertain (or just guess) which might be applicable.

Y: When ... does the series converge?

Pause.

Z: In other words, what is the value of ... of x or n - what is the value of n when ... is that what it means?

Y: I think so. I wouldn't like to commit myself, but ...! Right ...

Pause.

Y: Because you've got that ... if that's ... oh, hang on.

Z: It's not one of these erm, thingies, is it?

Y: Whaties?

Z: Like one of those theorems that we've been doing. You know we did, you did, "it looks approximately like ..."

Y: Oh, yes. Oh, what on earth did we do? I don't know.

Z: You know the, u_n and v_n. [*This notation was used for the limit comparison test in the students' course.*]

Y: Yes. Oh, it might be ...

Z: I don't know. Shall we try?

Y: Okay. Got to write something!

Z: You must end up with like, blank pieces of paper!

Y: Okay. Now which one's which?

Z: u_n is that. And v_n is ... isn't it?

Y: Yes.

Z: I don't know I was thinking that was ...

Y: I think that's right isn't it? I think it's 1 over n. I think. Let's say that, okay? It's better than anything else. And then is it, u_n over v_n?

Z: The v_n ... I don't know. Do we make it ... is that really helping?

Asked about what they were writing at this point, Zoë commented that they were stuck and Yvonne recalled that she could "do it with the notes". When later asked, they seemed flummoxed by the question of what it *means* for a series to converge.

We saw a different case in a recent tutorial, in which first year students expressed a wish to discuss the following question from a linear algebra problem sheet:

Let S be a basis for a vector space V and W be a subspace of V. Must there be a subset of S that is a basis of W? If so, give a proof; if not, give a counterexample.

Many sophisticated mathematicians might take a semantic approach to this, thinking of examples of vector spaces, subspaces and bases and perhaps manipulating them to seek or construct a counterexample. Indeed, the phrasing of the question ("if not, give a counterexample") could be seen as suggesting this approach. In the tutorial, however, the students had no idea how to begin. When then asked merely to give an example of a vector space, none of the seven appeared able to answer, despite much experience with various examples like $\mathbb{R}^3$ and with calculations in these spaces.

In this case, these students seemed to have *both* problems. First, they seemed to be expecting questions that required calculations using particular vectors, but were comparatively unaccustomed to questions about general concepts and found nothing to operate on in the question. Second, even when prompted, they had great difficulty in thinking about *a* vector space and *a* basis and *a* subspace as unified objects about whose relationships a question like this could be asked. The idea of considering examples seemed sensible to them when it was suggested, but they were not readily able to give examples of objects at this level of abstraction.

3.3.2   Access to a suitable example space

Of course, being able to evoke *an* example may not be sufficient. One could imagine, in the vector spaces task, that a person may be led astray by limited knowledge. If only "canonical" examples come to mind, one may think of $V = \mathbb{R}^3$ with its standard basis $\{(1,0,0),(0,1,0),(0,0,1)\}$, and a subspace $W = \mathbb{R}^2$ with basis $\{(1,0,0),(0,1,0)\}$ and conclude that a subset of the basis does indeed form a basis for the subspace (perhaps trying to construct some argument based on restricting the basis for the space to only those vectors from the subspace). This conclusion is simply wrong because it does not necessarily hold for other bases or subspaces, but it may make sense to someone who is able to think of vector spaces as objects but whose associated concept image is based on limited experience in which canonical examples have dominated.

One way to characterise what is needed here is to say that in order to use a semantic strategy effectively one needs to have access to a sufficiently well developed collection of examples or *example space* (in the sense of Watson & Mason, 2005) for the concept under consideration. An individual's accessible example space for a concept may sensibly be thought of as part of their concept image. Without a well-developed example space, one is more likely to conclude something is generally true when it holds only for a subset of the objects in question, or to construct an argument that implicitly relies on properties other than those contained in the definition. Illustrations of this phenomenon can be seen in the following student attempts to argue that every convergent sequence is bounded (see also Alcock & Simpson, 2002; Alcock & Simpson, 2004).

Wendy based her justification on sketches, saying:

W: It's convergent [*she draws a monotonic, increasing convergent sequence*]... yes, so if it's convergent, it's always ... or ... say it could be the other way round. It could be going down this way [*draws a monotonic decreasing convergent sequence*]. It converges, so it's always above that limit.

Wendy's argument would have been a reasonable beginning for a semantic proof attempt if all convergent sequences were monotonic. Of course they are not, but it is not hard to imagine that many of those Wendy had encountered might have been.

Cary, in a separate interview, did better, drawing a diagram like that in Figure 3.1 and varying the examples he considered in a deliberate attempt to identify properties that could be used to give a justification.

C: I've drawn ... er ... convergent sequences, such that .... I don't know, we have er, curves er ... approaching a limit but never quite reaching it, from above and below, and oscillating either side. I think that's pretty much what I've done. I was trying to think if there was a sequence which converges yet is unbounded both sides. But there isn't one. Because that would be ... because then it wouldn't converge.

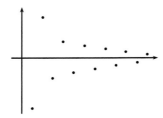

Figure 3.1: Cary's diagram

C: If it converges, that has to be ... well I don't suppose
    you can say bounded. It doesn't have to be monotonic
    . . .

C: Yes I'm trying to think if there's like ... if you can say
    the first term is, like, the highest or lowest bound, but
    it's not. Because then you could just make a sequence
    that happens to go, to do a loop up, or something like
    that.

Cary's reasoning feels more mathematically mature because
he showed better awareness of the range of possible variation
among convergent sequences; more so because he deliberately
considered such variation and tried to find an argument based
on properties that hold for all convergent sequences. Of course,
such effort is still not good enough to construct a formal proof if
it does not eventually make use of standard definitions or known
results.

3.3.3 Translating into a general, formal proof

A well-developed example space is not necessarily sufficient to make a semantic approach successful, because it may remain difficult to translate the understanding or insight gained by exploring examples into an appropriate formal proof. An obvious instance of this was presented in the introduction to this chapter. Most people agree that Brad seemed to understand why a strictly increasing real function cannot have a global maximum, but despite some effort he failed to translate this into a proof. It is as though he couldn't make the notation do what he wanted it to do, even though he understood what Raman calls the "key idea" (Raman, 2003).

In order to successfully produce a proof using a semantic approach, one needs to translate an example-based argument, which may be based on the relationships between any properties noticed while exploring one's example space, into deductions that relate formal definitions to one another. This brings us back to the importance of being able to accurately recall definitions (and suitable theorems) as well as co-ordinate their manipulation in a way which reflects the insights obtained from exploring the example space. This will obviously be a challenge for undergraduate students who have not understood the importance of definitions in advanced mathematics (as in Chapter 1), but it may also be inherently difficult because examples do not necessarily have a linear structure, while proofs do.

For instance, the image in Figure 3.2 might be drawn in order to support an argument that an increasing, bounded sequence must converge. However, it could just as easily be thought of

Figure 3.2: Bounded and convergent

as showing that an increasing, convergent sequence must be bounded. Getting from such an image to a formal argument depends upon being able to impose a linear structure upon one's thoughts about the image. This might well involve subtle properties (such as completeness, in the above case) that are far from obvious in the image, and it certainly involves having a good grasp of what can vary. For instance, the image does *not* show that a bounded, convergent sequence must be increasing.

Incidentally, this issue of imposing linear structure does not just apply to examples in the form of graphical images. The Cayley table for the group D_3 has each element appearing once in each row, for instance, but articulating a reason for this depends upon being able to construct an argument based on the group axioms, which is far from immediately obvious. At a simpler level, the numbers 17, 19 and 23 are all both prime and odd, but there is nothing in their usual representation that indicates which of these properties implies the other or how general such a relationship is.

In general, there is considerable evidence that students often do not have a very useful conception of what it means to give a mathematical proof, and that they often try to base arguments on more or less sophisticated versions of example-based empirical reasoning similar to that seen above (Balacheff, 1987; Bell, 1976; Chazan, 1993; Galbraith, 1981; Harel & Sowder, 1998). There is also some evidence that this strategy becomes less prevalent as students proceed through a degree, with more recognition of the status of definition-based arguments (Segal, 2000). However, it remains difficult for students to construct or critically evaluate such formal arguments, some reasons for which are discussed in the next section.

3.4   Using a syntactic strategy

In order to successfully apply a syntactic strategy to prove a given statement, one needs to:

1. Recognise that this strategy is applicable;

2. Recognise structure at an appropriate level;

3. Use logical language correctly and make valid deductions;

4. Structure an argument appropriately.

Again, we discuss each of these in turn.

3.4.1   Recognising that a syntactic strategy is applicable

As we saw with the semantic strategy, particular contexts (for particular people) may make it difficult to recognise even that a particular strategy is worth exploring. In the semantic case, examples may not be readily accessible. In the syntactic case, more or less the opposite problem occurs: a statement may involve such familiar ideas that the student is either unconvinced that any proof is needed or unable to see how one could be given. This occurs particularly when:

- The requirement is to prove something which has been known and accepted for a long time;

- The requirement is to prove something which seems trivially true.

A classic instance of the first case is that in which students are asked to work with the axioms of the real numbers to prove, for instance, that $-1 < 0$ or that 1 is the unique multiplicative identity. Such things have been "known" to undergraduates for many years and have been accorded the same status as similar statements that now function as axioms; it requires a new type of discipline to recognise such imposed distinctions between what is now taken as axiomatic and what must be proved. A classic example of the second case is provided by the intermediate value theorem. A glance at a diagram convinces most students that this theorem is "obviously" true (from a semantic viewpoint), but it has a long and complicated proof involving the completeness axiom. In general, support may be needed to help students recognise that in addition to establishing truth, we are also interesting in systematising our results (Bell, 1976). We discuss this further in the Responses section.

3.4.2 Recognising structure at an appropriate level

The second issue also parallels one in the section on semantic reasoning. There we observed that students may be reading mathematical statements primarily in the expectation of finding "cues" to perform a certain procedure. In working syntactically this search for cues is also problematic, largely because it is essential at this stage to carefully read the statement under consideration in order to be clear about what is being asked. At least some of our students appear to expect to take a mathematical sentence with words and symbols in it, pretty much ignore the words, write down the symbols, then perform a standard sequence of manipulations on the symbols in order to arrive at some standard form of conclusion. This does involve making use of the regularities in syntactic structure of mathematical statements and manipulations, but it is not what we mean by syntactic reasoning here as it operates at nothing like a high enough level. Our meaning of syntactic reasoning involves dealing with whole statements, proofs and even chains of proofs at a structural level, not just snippets of definitions. Indeed, it may be that a student fails to accord sufficient importance to a minor notational difference that has large implications for meaning, as is the case in this quote from a mathematician (Alcock, 2008):

> For instance yesterday one student was complaining because in proving ... in proving that the sum of an even integer and an odd integer is odd, she had begun by saying "let x and y be integers, assume x is even and y is odd", then she wrote "x equal $2a$, and y equal $2a + 1$". Then eventually of course she ended up with $x + y$ equal an even number, which is two times something, plus 1. And I marked the proof wrong. And then she was asking "why is it wrong?" I said "because your proof, it follows from what you said in your proof, that if x is an arbitrary even integer and y is an arbitrary odd integer then $y = x + 1$". And then she said, "but I thought that what I had to do was end up with $x + y$ equal to two times something plus 1, and I did".

A more subtle illustration of what might go wrong if one does not attend to structure at the appropriate level is provided by the case of Xavier, who was working with Wendy on the *convergent implies bounded* problem discussed earlier. Xavier was more focused on representations related to the appropriate definitions, but at the level of detail of the notation. This can be seen in his comment,

> X: Isn't it something to do with that ... a_n minus l, don't you remember?

Xavier then went on to attempt to construct an argument. One can see that he remembered only snippets of the definition, that he was prone to mis-statements in his speech (in this excerpt below he said "e" when he meant "epsilon" and confused his "l" for a digit "1") and that his use of the logical language was imprecise.

> X: Er, the term in the sequence, a_n, minus the limit ... the modulus of that is less than epsilon where epsilon ... is ... any real number ... and n is beyond any big N in the sequence. So then all the terms beyond large N. And then if you get rid of the modulus sign, you can write that a minus epsilon is less than a to the n minus one, is less than epsilon, and that can be rearranged so that a to the n is less than e plus one, but it's also greater than one minus epsilon ...

More importantly, after the above excerpt, Xavier concluded,

> X: So therefore a to the n is bounded above and below, and therefore this is the definition for the convergent sequence. So it converges.

In making this conclusion it is clear that he had lost track of what it was he was trying to prove and had not made precise links between the relevant definitions (see also Alcock & Simpson, 2005). It appears that he was taking something of a syntactic approach, but focussed on the recollection of short strings of symbols, rather than whole statements, or the structure of arguments.

3.4.3 Language and deductions

Of course, it is not the case that there are no cues in mathematical statements as to ways to proceed, but they occur at
a higher structural level than students may be used to and it
is necessary to correctly interpret logical language in order to
identify and use them.

A first point, as discussed in Chapter 1, is that of definitions.
If a student doesn't know that *show that every convergent sequence is bounded* means *show that a general sequence that satisfies the definition of convergence also satisfies the definition of
boundedness,* then they will have little chance of working successfully with the syntactic strategy. A second issue is that, just
as the use of concept-words in mathematics sometimes differs
from that in everyday language, so does the use of the logical
terminology in which sentences are phrased. Two commonly
cited and very important instances of this are *if . . . then* statements and "∀∃" and "∃∀" statements. In everyday language,
context plays a large role in determining the intended meaning of statements including the word "if". For instance, a child
told, "If you are good, you will get some sweets" can reasonably
conclude that if they are not good they will not get sweets, and
that if they get some sweets, they must have been good. In
other words, they can interpret the statement as an *if and only
if* statement. In addition, Dubinsky & Yiparaki (2000) found
that most students in their study could not distinguish between
"∀∃" and "∃∀" statements in mathematics and, indeed, tended
to discuss the concepts involved in a general way, rather than
look at the truth value of the particular statement. A further

instance is the use of the word "so", as described by a mathematician in Alcock (2008):

> ... students who would say, "we want to prove this, so that" - it was never clear to me whether they meant "so we can conclude that", or "so we need to verify that". And there were a lot of proofs which would be correct, if I could only infer that they meant "so we need to verify ... so we need to verify ... so we need to verify ... and then this last one is clearly true so everything stacks up."

In all of these cases, mathematicians use this terminology in a way that is less ambiguous than its use in everyday language. In general, however, mathematical statements are not given in fully formal terms and there can be a good deal of interpretation to do in order to determine the logical structure of a statement. Selden & Selden (1995) examined students' logical interpretations of relatively standard statements from calculus. They found that students often did not give correct "unpackings", for example, when reading a statement like:

> A function f is increasing on an interval I means that for any numbers x_1 and x_2 in I, if $x_1 < x_2$ then $f(x_1) < f(x_2)$,

students might unpack this, beginning with

$$(\exists f \in F)((f \text{ is increasing}) \dots$$

apparently seeing the statement being about a single function rather than about all functions.

Such incorrect interpretations of mathematical language can lead to incorrect application of theorems. An instance of this reported by Hazzan & Leron (1996), in which students misused Lagrange's theorem to conclude that $\mathbb{Z}_3$ is a subgroup of $\mathbb{Z}_6$ because 3 divides 6. As Hazzan pointed out,

> By giving this answer, students not only confuse Lagrange's theorem with its converse (*If $k|o(G)$, then there exists in G a subgroup of order k* – which is not a true statement), but actually use an *incorrect* version of the converse statement (*If $o(H)|o(G)$ then H is a subgroup of G*). (Hazzan, 1999, p.78)

We are aware that to a mathematician it may well seem that this kind of logical reasoning ought to be straightforward, but research in the psychology of reasoning shows that this is not the case, even in simple situations (Johnson-Laird & Byrne, 1991; Evans, 2007). To those who are inclined to think that we should not be teaching advanced mathematics to those who cannot get this kind of reasoning right, we offer a cautionary note: studies by Inglis & Simpson (2004) suggest that while mathematics students and mathematicians perform better than general "intelligent" populations at well-known and apparently straightforward logical reasoning tasks, they are far from perfect at them, despite the assumptions by many in mathematics and mathematics education that they should be (e.g. Devlin, 2000). Perhaps mathematicians learn to make correct logical deductions not by thinking about logic in the abstract, but by making deductions in context, learning the language routines of the field and/or by combining syntactic and semantic work. However this skill is developed, to use a syntactic strategy successfully, means that one needs to be able to get from one statement to another in a way which fits the accepted "grammar" of mathematics.

3.4.4 Structuring an argument

Unfortunately, being able to interpret statements correctly and make correct deductions can still be insufficient, since it does not necessarily tell us which deductions to make. Linguistic cues can help overcome this problem, providing an element of the structure the syntactic strategy relies on. For instance, the global structure of the statement to be proved might indicate a potentially appropriate overall strategy:

- *If ... then* indicates that one might begin by writing down the definitions relevant to the premises and try to derive the conclusion from these, or by assuming the premises and the negation of the conclusion and aiming for a contradiction.

- *For all* can act as a cue to begin, "Let x be a .... From the definition, x is ...".

- *There exists* can act as a cue to construct an example with a property or to try showing that the object's nonexistence leads to a contradiction (starting with "Suppose every x in ... was not ... ").

- *And* needs to act as a cue for combining definitions. It is sometimes implicit (as in "prove that an increasing, bounded sequence is convergent").

Indeed, the cues in the statement may go well beyond giving a starting point. Selden & Selden (1995) suggested that, in many cases, there are whole proof frameworks which can be derived from the statement for those taking a syntactic approach and which give the structure of the proof (often independent of the mathematical context). They gave the example of proving the theorem:

> For every semigroup S and every group G, if S is compact and G is a subgroup of S, then there is a group H such that H is a subgroup of S, G is a subgroup of H, and H is maximal and closed.

The proof framework for this, they suggested, is:

> **Proof:** Let S be a semigroup and let G be a group. Suppose S is compact and G is a subgroup of S. _____. Let H be _____. Then H is a subgroup of S because _____. Also G is a subgroup of H because _____. H is closed because _____ and H is maximal because _____.

which one could arguably arrive at with no understanding of 'group', 'compact' etc.

Some students, like Carla in the introduction, clearly pick up at least some of these cues. Others, however, may not: where a mathematician might look at this framework and think "Well, of course the proof must go something like that," a student might be unable to identify appropriate cues or may use them inappropriately because of incorrect interpretations of the logical language as above.

Moreover, having an overall structure like this is very helpful, but it still may not be easy to fill in the gaps. Topic-specific *strategic knowledge* may also be necessary. Weber (2001) used this term to highlight differences in performance between undergraduates and more experienced mathematicians in proving elementary but non-trivial propositions in group theory. He found that the undergraduates often knew all the information that would be necessary to construct a proof, but failed to do so because unlike those with more experience, they did not readily recognise situations in which (for instance) a particular isomorphism theorem would be useful.

Finally, there are other cues which may support a successful syntactic approach and not all of these are strictly mathematical. Many students notice that we normally ask them to prove things from just the right set of properties and they can become confused when we ask questions which include irrelevant properties (e.g. "prove that every odd prime is the sum of two consecutive integers"). Such social conventions can be very useful for undergraduate success, but coming to rely upon them can be the undoing of later independent graduate work (Duffin & Simpson, 2005).

3.5   Responses: Addressing these issues

In this section we discuss two ways in which our teaching is influenced by thinking in terms of the distinction between semantic and syntactic reasoning. First, as in the Responses sections at the end of the other two chapters, we describe how the distinction frames our thinking about teaching strategies at the small and large scales. In doing so we discuss semantic and syntactic reasoning separately for clarity. However, we believe that it is important for students to become fluent in using both strategies, because:

- Semantic reasoning can give quick and "intuitive" insight, but is prone to errors of overgeneralisation and does not lead directly to written proofs;

- Syntactic reasoning does lead to written proofs based on accepted information, but does not necessarily include a mechanism for choosing which inferences to make.

Indeed, it may be that a key to success at this level is to be able to move fluently between the two strategies depending upon the goal and demands of the mathematical situation.

We develop this point in the second part of our discussion, which focuses on the way in which thinking in these terms has improved our sensitivity as teachers. We briefly discuss research which indicates that at least some individuals (from undergraduates to successful mathematicians) tend to preferentially use one or the other strategy. As teachers this awareness has helped us become more alert to cases in which a student is pursuing a strategy that we think is somewhat unproductive under the circumstances, but that may be mathematically legitimate (at least, perhaps, in some stronger form), and to help them move on from where they are rather than dismissing their work. We find this to be especially useful in cases in which the students' tendency is different from our own, and we conclude this chapter by noting that the most important thing might be to help students recognise the strengths and weaknesses of the strategies and make sensible choices about when to use which.

3.5.1 Developing skills associated with semantic reasoning

In the sections above we noted that to use a semantic strategy successfully one needs to:

1. Recognise that this strategy is applicable;

2. Have access to a suitable example space;

3. Be able to translate insight gained by thinking about examples into a general, formal proof.

A first thing to recognise, then, is that many students probably do not spontaneously think about examples when faced with a new definition and/or statement, so that if we want them to develop this habit we will have to do something about it. A second is that even if they do think of examples, the range of these might not be very broad. These points are obviously related to Chapter 1 discussion about concept images, in which we noted that exposure to a wider range of examples may therefore be appropriate. Here we expand this point by discussing particular tasks that might be used to structure such experience.

In an interview, one mathematician talked about the tasks he used to encourage students to think in a similar way.

> So, what I've been trying to do is to have these exercises where the whole purpose of the exercise is just for them to process a mathematical definition. . . . So, it just sort of asks them questions about the definition. Not deep questions at all. . . . I have one where I just define what a partition of a set means. I define it formally, so it has these two conditions, a collection of subsets, such that the empty set is not one of the subsets, for every element of the underlying set there is a subset that contains it, for any two sets in the partition the intersection is empty. Which is pretty abstract, when you look at something like that. And then I just ask okay, construct three examples of a partition on the set $\{1,2,3,4,5\}$. And then, okay, construct an example of a collection of sets on $\{1,2,3,4,5\}$ which satisfies the first two properties but not the third. The first and the third properties but not the second, the second and the third properties but not the first.

Watson and Mason have discussed similar ideas very systematically, giving a variety of ways in which we might encourage the appropriate development of example spaces. They include various tasks designed to push students towards generalising beyond the first examples they think of, such as:

- Write down a function that is continuous at one point;
- Write down another;
- Write down one that has a different kind of discontinuity at a point;
- What other kinds of discontinuity can you make?

(Watson & Mason, 2005, p.17)

Mason has also discussed very structured example generation tasks in undergraduate level material:

- Write down a function specified on $[0, 1]$;
- Write down a function which is also continuous on $[0, 1]$;
- Write down a function which is also differentiable on $[0, 1]$;
- Write down a function which also has its extremal values at the ends of the interval;
- Write down a function which also has a local maximum in the interior of the interval;
- Write down a function which also has a local minimum in the interior of the interval.

Now go back and make sure that, at each stage, the example you provided is not also an example at the

> following stage. For example, your first function can-
> not be continuous on $[0, 1]$. (Mason, 2002, p.14)

Tasks of this nature are designed to help students to go beyond "standard" examples and to recognise what Watson and
Mason call *boundary examples* and *dimensions of possible variation*. These goals have significance for the third of our points
about what is necessary for successful use of a semantic strategy, because making translations between what is noticed when
referring to examples and a general argument requires what Mason & Pimm (1984) called seeing the general in the particular.
Being able to do this depends on being able to see what might
vary without changing one or more key properties of the example. One of Mason and Pimm's main points is that where a
lecturer looks at a single example and sees it as representative
of a whole class of examples to which some argument applies, a
student may look at a single example and see precisely that: a
single example.

The issue of seeing an example as generic has been taken
up by various authors, and it has been suggested that an argument based on a generic example can be more convincing
for students than a general one. Tall (1979), for instance, discussed a situation in which students considered many different
arguments about irrationality of square roots. He found that
the most favoured argument was one which involved looking at
a generic example of a rational (5/8) and what happens to the
prime factorisation of numerator and denominator (the doubling
of factors) when the rational is squared. Rowland (2001) cited
similar experience of improved understanding of the proof that

every prime number has a primitive root when this was presented in a generic version using the number 19 (he also gave a discussion of many other generic proofs). Of course, such arguments are not the same as general proofs, and Rowland noted that students may understand such an argument but still have difficulty in working with notation appropriately to give a general proof. However, we have also had some success with tasks that ask questions leading to an argument about a particular example (seen as generic) and then ask for a general version of the argument.

It is undoubtedly useful in abstract mathematics to be able to build an example space that accurately represents the extension of a concept definition, and to treat examples from this space as generic when constructing and understanding arguments. However, in concluding this section we note again that there are competing values at work, since we also want our students to think beyond examples and learn to develop general arguments based on formal definitions. They must, therefore, develop some skills associated with syntactic reasoning.

3.5.2 Developing skills associated with syntactic reasoning

In the sections above we noted that to use a syntactic strategy successfully one needs to:

1. Recognise that this strategy is applicable;

2. Recognise structure at an appropriate level;

3. Use logical language correctly and make valid deductions;

4. Structure an argument appropriately.

Addressing the first two of these is obviously also related to the discussion about definitions in Chapter 1. Students need to learn that our arguments are based on definitions (and axioms), so they must learn to invoke these appropriately and to recognise where these are used in proofs. As we discussed, it can be hard to recognise such definitions and structures, especially in situations in which one is dealing with very familiar concepts. One thing we do to address this is to make distinctions within proving activity, acknowledging that we sometimes prove "obvious" results and explaining this in terms of what Bell (1976) called the *systematisation* function of proof as well as its role in verification and in illumination. Weber (2002) made a similar distinction, identifying a *proof that justifies the use of a definition* as one in which the conclusion is regarded as obvious and it is the assumptions that are in question, and a *proof that illustrates a technique* in which the purpose is not to prove a given statement so much as to demonstrate how to prove statements of that type.

A different kind of intervention designed to address the same problem was suggested by Selwyn (1980), and involves temporarily obscuring the familiarity of the rational number system, introducing this system as "Noitcarf numbers" (pairs of integers $(a, b), a \neq 0$ to disguise $\frac{b}{a}$) with associated axioms (such as $(a, b) \odot (c, d) = (ac, bc + ad)$ to disguise addition). We have found in our classes that when asking students to prove things in this obscured system (such as that (n, n) acts as an identity in the system), they have far fewer difficulties in overcoming the "obviousness" which would attend asking students to prove that 1 is the multiplicative identity of $\mathbb{Q}$.

In addressing the second two points, we note that traditionally universities try to teach the validity of deductions through the teaching of formal logic, but there is some evidence that this has little effect on making such deductions (Cheng et al., 1986). Indeed, as Inglis & Simpson (2004) found there is some evidence that mathematicians may not do their mathematics by using formal logic either. This does not mean that teaching formal logic has no intrinsic value, but learning about truth tables may well not have the desired effect upon students' ability to correctly interpret and work with mathematical statement in a content area. Another interesting approach, recommended by Epp (2003), is to make specific effort to highlight and contrast situations in mathematics and in everyday language in which valid interpretations of logical connectives are either the same or distinct.

At the level of particular types of proof, various suggestions have been made of ways to improve students' understanding of structure. Leron (1985), for example, pointed out that contradiction proofs involve working for the majority of the proof with false statements, and suggested separating out the "construction" part of such a proof first (e. g. starting from a set of primes, showing that there is a prime not in that set before working towards a contradiction of the statement there is a finite number of primes). Harel (2001) has done considerable work on proof by induction, especially in designing and researching tasks that lead naturally toward inductive arguments rather than teaching induction as a standard procedure first. Although the focus is on structure in both of these cases, they involve at least some degree of consideration of examples and so might be considered a semantic approach to highlighting this syntactic structure. Weber (2006), on the other hand, was concerned with the strategic knowledge that is necessary to construct proofs even if one has a good grasp of logic and knowledge of the appropriate theorems. He reported a small-scale study in which students were explicitly taught syntactic strategies for proving theorems in group theory without any emphasis on semantic aspects, and were able to prove significantly more theorems as a result.

Of course, there are numerous books that aim specifically to teach students how to interpret written mathematics and how to reason logically in a way that is appropriate. Texts by both Exner (1996) and Solow (2005) explicitly address many of the common problems that we cited in earlier sections of this chapter. As a final note on this point, we have observed that one is unlikely to insult a whole class of first years by saying "This is the premise, and this is the conclusion, and we are (as always) going to assume that the premise is true and show that the conclusion follows from it." On the contrary, many appreciate this type of comment.

3.5.3 Preferences for different strategies

As we noted above, successful mathematicians use both syntactic and semantic strategies and combine them effectively. Indeed, most probably refer to both in their teaching (Weber, 2004). However, introspective reports (MacLane, 1993; Hal-

mos, 1985) and, to some degree, larger-scale surveys indicate
that mathematicians recognise different approaches among their
colleagues that are consistent with our descriptions of semantic
and syntactic reasoning. Poincaré, for instance, wrote that

> It is impossible to study the works of the great math-
> ematicians, or even those of the lesser, without notic-
> ing and distinguishing two opposite tendencies, or
> rather two entirely different kinds of minds. The
> one sort are above all occupied with logic; to read
> their works, one is tempted to believe they have ad-
> vanced only step by step. The other sort are guided
> by intuition and at the first stroke make quick but
> sometimes precarious conquests.
> (Poincaré, 1913, p.210)

In giving presentations about student reasoning to mathematicians we have heard an argument start up in the audience,
where one mathematician effectively says "Mathematics is not
about the symbols, it's about understanding the meaning be-
hind the symbols! You can't possibly be said to understand
if all you can do is perform procedures!". However, a second
mathematician counters with something like: "No, no, no, the
whole point and power of abstract mathematics is precisely that
you *can* work with the symbols without having to think about
any specific instantiations of the concepts!"

Of course, these two claims are not actually contradictory,
but they serve to highlight quite different emphases in thinking

about mathematics, and it is not hard to see that they might lead to quite different emphases in teaching (Alcock, 2008).

For us as teachers, the real significance of this is that if students have preferences too, then this raises the possibility of clashes between what a student is looking for when they are trying to learn mathematics, and what their lecturer thinks they ought to be doing. A small amount of research on actual responses to proof questions (rather than self-reports) indicates that at least some students have quite distinct tendencies to use either a semantic or a syntactic strategy. These include studies in real analysis (Alcock & Simpson, 2004; Pinto & Tall, 2002), in group theory (Weber & Alcock, 2004), and in transition to proof courses (Alcock & Weber, 2008) at the undergraduate level and across the postgraduate level (Duffin & Simpson, 2005). In view of this, in our own lectures we now work harder at using both types of strategy and at making distinctions regarding which is good for what. We are also more careful in small-group or one-to-one tutorials to attend to students' apparent preferences, and to avoid making giant, unexplained leaps with our hints and suggestions (if a student is struggling to work with new symbols via a familiar syntactic strategy, it may be that an incitement to "look at some examples" simply piles more work of an even less comfortable kind on top of existing difficulties).

Of course, although we try to address both strategies, we recognise that there is an asymmetry in what is required, at least at the undergraduate level. A student accustomed to working in a syntactic way could, provided that they recognise the structures at the appropriate level, pass many undergraduate exams with minimal need to engage with a wide range of examples for every concept they meet. A student accustomed to working in a semantic way could probably not, however, succeed in producing appropriate proofs, no matter how many examples they became conversant with. This is an interesting point because Semadeni (2007) argued that, in fact, a well developed concept image or example space (what he called *deep intuition*) allows one to function as well as someone with a full knowledge of definitions – or, indeed, better where different definitions are interchangeable (such as the triangle defined by its vertices, its sides, its area set etc.) or where syntactic inconsistencies are overlooked (such as whether a zero x_0 of a function f is identified with the point $(x_0, 0)$ on a graph).

However, it remains the case that an undergraduate student is expected to handle rather particular kinds of proofs within pre-set systems of axioms, definitions and theorems. A certain mastery of the syntax of mathematics is therefore necessary for success. This does not mean that a student would have to abandon a semantic strategy, but they must learn to translate their thinking into appropriate terms. This may not be easy and one final thing that thinking in these terms has led us to change is our attention to detail in explaining such translations. Although it has always been the case that we tend to draw diagrams as well as give formal proofs (especially in analysis), we now expend considerably more effort in explaining precisely how the various symbols used in the theorems, definition and proof correspond to labels on the diagram, and how we knew where to put those labels. It is not clear that this has the desired effect for all students, as for every student who says "oh, I understand it now!" there is another who claims an aversion to any kind of diagram. However, it is our hope that highlighting this type of link benefits at least some students with a tendency to favour either approach by helping them to recognise links with other ways of thinking.

Bibliography

Alcock, L. (2008). Mathematicians' perspectives on the teaching and learning of proof. In F. Hitt, D. A. Holton, & P. Thompson (Eds.), *Research in Collegiate Mathematics VII* (pp. 73–100). Providence, RI: American Mathematical Society.

Alcock, L. & Simpson, A. (2002). Definitions: dealing with categories mathematically. *For the Learning of Mathematics*, *22*(2), 28–34.

Alcock, L. & Simpson, A. (2004). Convergence of sequences and series: Interactions between visual reasoning and the learner's beliefs about their own role. *Educational Studies in Mathematics*, *57*, 1–32.

Alcock, L. & Simpson, A. (2005). Convergence of sequences and series 2: Interactions between nonvisual reasoning and the learner's beliefs about their own role. *Educational Studies in Mathematics*, *58*, 77–100.

Alcock, L. & Weber, K. (2008). Referential and syntactic approaches to proving: Case studies from a transition-to-proof course. In F. Hitt, D. A. Holton, & P. Thompson (Eds.), *Research in Collegiate Mathematics VII* (pp. 101–123). Providence, RI: American Mathematical Society.

Asiala, M., Brown, A., Devries, D. J., Dubinsky, E., Mathews, E., & Thomas, K. (1996). A framework for research and curriculum development in undergraduate mathematics education. In J. Kaput, A. H. Schoenfeld, & E. Dubinsky (Eds.), *Research in Collegiate Mathematics II* (pp. 1–32). Providence, RI: American Mathematical Society.

Balacheff, N. (1987). Processus de preuves et situations de validation. *Educational Studies in Mathematics, 18,* 147–176.

Bell, A. W. (1976). A study of pupils' proof conceptions in mathematical situations. *Educational Studies in Mathematics, 7,* 23–40.

Breidenbach, D., Dubinsky, E., Hawks, J., & Nichols, D. (1992). Development of the process conception of function. *Educational Studies in Mathematics, 23,* 247–285.

Chazan, D. (1993). High school geometry students' justification for their views of empirical evidence and mathematical proof. *Educational Studies in Mathematics, 24,* 359–387.

Cheng, P. W., Holyoak, K. J., Nisbett, R. E., & Oliver, L. M. (1986). Pragmatic versus syntactic approaches to training deductive reasoning. *Cognitive Psychology, 18,* 293–328.

Cornu, B. (1991). Limits. In D. O. Tall (Ed.), *Advanced Mathematical Thinking* chapter 10, (pp. 153–166). Dordrecht: Kluwer.

Cottrill, J., Dubinsky, E., Nichols, D., Schwingendorf, K.,

Thomas, K., & Vidakovic, D. (1996). Understanding the limit concept: Beginning with a coordinated process scheme. *Journal of Mathematical Behavior, 15*, 167–192.

Dahlberg, R. P. & Housman, D. L. (1997). Facilitating learning events through example generation. *Educational Studies in Mathematics, 33*, 283–299.

Davis, R. B. & Vinner, S. (1986). The notion of limit: Some seemingly unavoidable misconception stages. *Journal of Mathematical Behavior, 5*, 281–303.

Devlin, K. (2000). *The Maths Gene: Why everybody has it, but most people don't use it.* London: Orion Books.

Dubinsky, E. (1987). On teaching mathematical induction, I. *Journal of Mathematical Behavior, 6*(1), 305–317.

Dubinsky, E. (1989). On teaching mathematical induction, II. *Journal of Mathematical Behavior, 8*, 285–304.

Dubinsky, E. (1991). Reflective abstraction in advanced mathematical thinking. In D. O. Tall (Ed.), *Advanced Mathematical Thinking* chapter 7, (pp. 95–123). Dordrecht: Kluwer.

Dubinsky, E., Elterman, F., & Gong, C. (1988). The student's construction of quantification. *For the Learning of Mathematics, 8*(2), 44–51.

Dubinsky, E. & Harel, G. (1992). The nature of the process conception of function. In G. Harel & E. Dubinsky (Eds.), *The concept of function: Aspects of epistemology and pedagogy, MAA Notes 25* (pp. 85–106). Washington, DC: MAA.

Dubinsky, E., Leron, U., Dautermann, J., & Zazkis, R. (1994).

On learning fundamental concepts of group theory. *Educational Studies in Mathematics, 27*, 153–174.

Dubinsky, E. & Yiparaki, O. (2000). On student understanding of ∀∃ and ∃∀ quantification. In E. Dubinsky, A. H. Schoenfeld, & J. Kaput (Eds.), *Research in Collegiate Mathematics IV* (pp. 239–289). Providence, RI: American Mathematical Society.

Duffin, J. & Simpson, A. (2005). Cognitive empathy and the transition to independent graduate study in mathematics. *Educational Studies in Mathematics, 58*, 121–135.

Edwards, B. S. & Ward, M. B. (2004). Surprises from mathematics education research: Student (mis)use of mathematical definitions. *American Mathematical Monthly, 111*, 411–424.

Epp, S. (2003). The role of logic in teaching proof. *American Mathematical Monthly, 110*, 886–899.

Evans, J. St. B. T. (2007). *Hypothetical Thinking: Dual Processes in Reasoning and Judgement.* Hove, UK: Psychology Press.

Exner, G. R. (1996). *An Accompaniment to Higher Mathematics.* New York: Springer.

Galbraith, P. L. (1981). Aspects of proving: A clinical investigation of process. *Educational Studies in Mathematics, 12*, 1–28.

Goldin, G. A. & Kaput, J. J. (1996). A joint perspective on the idea of representation in learning and doing mathematics. In L. Steffe, P. Nesher, P. Cobb, G. Golding, & B. Greer (Eds.), *Theories of mathematical learning* (pp. 397 – 430). Hillsdale,

N.J.: Erlbaum.

Gray, E. & Tall, D. (1994). Duality, ambiguity and flexibility: A proceptual view of simple arithmetic. *Journal for Research in Maths Education*, *25*, 115–141.

Halmos, P. R. (1985). *I Want to be a Mathematician*. New York: Springer.

Harel, G. (2001). The development of mathematical induction as a proof scheme: A model for dnr-based instruction. In S. Campbell & R. Zazkis (Eds.), *Learning and teaching number theory* (pp. 185–212). Westport, CT: Ablex Publishing Corp.

Harel, G. & Sowder, L. (1998). Students' proof schemes: Results from exploratory studies. In A. H. Schoenfeld, J. Kaput, & E. Dubinsky (Eds.), *Research in Collegiate Mathematics III* (pp. 234–282). Providence, RI: American Mathematical Society.

Hazzan, O. (1999). Reducing abstraction level when learning abstract algebra concepts. *Educational Studies in Mathematics*, *40*, 71–90.

Hazzan, O. & Leron, U. (1996). Students' use and misuse of mathematical theorems: The case of Lagrange's theorem. *For the Learning of Mathematics*, *16*(1), 23–26.

Inglis, M. & Simpson, A. (2004). Mathematicians and the selection task. In Johnsen Høines, M. & Fuglestad, A. B. (Eds.), *Proceedings of the 28th International Conference on the Psychology of Mathematics Education*, volume 3, (pp. 89–96)., Bergen, Norway. IGPME.

Johnson-Laird, P. N. & Byrne, R. M. J. (1991). *Deduction*. Hove, UK: Erlbaum.

Lakatos, I. (1976). *Proofs and Refutations*. Cambridge: CUP.

Leron, U. (1985). A direct approach to indirect proofs. *Educational Studies in Mathematics, 16*, 321–325.

MacLane, S. (1993). Responses to theoretical mathematics. *Bulletin of the American Mathematical Society, 30*, 190–191.

Mason, J. (2002). *Mathematics teaching practice: A guide for university and college lecturers*. Chichester: Horwood Publishing.

Mason, J. & Pimm, D. (1984). Generic examples: Seeing the general in the particular. *Educational Studies in Mathematics, 15*, 277–289.

Monaghan, J. (1991). Problems with the language of limits. *For the Learning of Mathematics, 11*(3), 20–24.

Pinto, M. & Tall, D. O. (2002). Building formal mathematics on visual imagery: A case study and a theory. *For the Learning of Mathematics, 22*(1), 2–10.

Poincaré, H. (1913). *The Foundations of Science* (University Press of America, 1982 ed.). New York: The Science Press.

Raman, M. (2003). Key ideas: What are they and how can they help us understand how people view proof? *Educational Studies in Mathematics, 52*, 319–325.

Robert, A. (1982). L'aquisition de la notion de convergence de suites numériques dans l'enseignement supérieur. *Recherches en Didactique des Mathématiques, 3*, 307–341.

Rowland, T. (2001). Generic proofs in number theory. In S. Campbell & R. Zazkis (Eds.), *Learning and teaching number theory: Research in cognition and instruction* (pp. 157–184). Westport, CT: Ablex Publishing.

Segal, J. (2000). Learning about mathematical proof: conviction and validity. *Journal of Mathematical Behavior*, *18*, 191–210.

Selden, J. & Selden, A. (1995). Unpacking the logic of mathematical statements. *Educational Studies in Mathematics*, *29*, 123–151.

Selwyn, J. (1980). Noitcraf numbers. *Mathematics Teaching*, *90*.

Semadeni, Z. (2007). Deep intuition as a level in the development of the concept image. *Educational Studies in Mathematics*, *68*, 1–17.

Sfard, A. (1991). On the dual nature of mathematical conceptions: Reflections on processes and objects as two sides of the same coin. *Educational Studies in Mathematics*, *22*, 1–36.

Slavitt, D. (1997). An alternate route to the reification of function. *Educational Studies in Mathematics*, *33*, 259–281.

Solow, D. (2005). *How to read and do proofs*. Chichester: John Wiley & Sons.

Tall, D. O. (1979). Cognitive aspects of proof, with special reference to the irrationality of $\sqrt{2}$. In *Proceedings of the 3rd International Conference on the Psychology of Mathematics Education*, (pp. 203–205)., Warwick, UK. IGPME.

Tall, D. O. & Vinner, S. (1981). Concept image and concept

definition in mathematics with particular reference to limits and continuity. *Educational Studies in Mathematics, 12*, 151–169.

Thurston, W. P. (1990). Mathematical education. *Notices of the American Mathematical Society, 37*, 844–850.

Thurston, W. P. (1994). On proof and progress in mathematics. *Bulletin of the American Mathematical Society, 30*, 161–177.

Vinner, S. (1976). The naive concept of definition in mathematics. *Educational Studies in Mathematics, 7*, 413–429.

Vinner, S. (1991). The role of definitions in teaching and learning. In D. O. Tall (Ed.), *Advanced Mathematical Thinking* chapter 5, (pp. 65–81). Dordrecht: Kluwer.

Vinner, S. & Dreyfus, T. (1989). Images and definitions for the concept of function. *Journal for Research in Mathematics Education, 20*, 356–366.

Watson, A. & Mason, J. (2005). *Mathematics as a constructive activity: Learners generating examples.* Mahwah, NJ: Lawrence Erlbaum Associates.

Weber, K. (2001). Student difficulty in constructing proofs: the need for strategic knowledge. *Educational Studies in Mathematics, 48*, 101–119.

Weber, K. (2002). Beyond convincing and explaining: Proofs that justify the use of definitions and axiomatic structures and proofs that illustrate technique. *For the Learning of Mathematics, 22*(3), 14–17.

Weber, K. (2006). Investigating and teaching the thought processes used to consruct proofs. In F. Hitt, G. Harel, A. Selden, & S. Hauk (Eds.), *Research in Collegiate Mathematics VI* (pp. 197–232). Providence, RI: American Mathematical Society.

Weber, K. & Alcock, L. (2004). Semantic and syntactic proof productions. *Educational Studies in Mathematics, 56,* 209–234.

Weyl, H. (1940). The mathematical way of thinking. *Science, 92,* 437–446.

Yackel, E., Rasmussen, C., & King, K. (2000). Social and sociomathematical norms in an advanced undergraduate mathematics course. *Journal of Mathematical Behavior, 19,* 275–287.

Zandieh, M., Larsen, S., & Nunley, D. (2008). Proving starting from informal notions of symmetry and transformations. In M. Carlson & C. Rasmussen (Eds.), *Making the connection: Research and Teaching in Undergraduate Mathematics* chapter 10, (pp. 125–138). Washington DC: MAA.